THE ROOTS OF
SCIENCE
AND ITS FRUITS

Books by the Author

Nuclear Physics

The Optical Model of Elastic Scattering, Oxford, 1963.
Nuclear Reactions and Nuclear Structure, Oxford, 1971.
Nuclear Heavy-Ion Reactions, Oxford, 1976.
Growth Points in Nuclear Physics, Vol. 1, Pergamon Press,1980.
Growth Points in Nuclear Physics, Vol. 2, Pergamon Press,1980.
Growth Points in Nuclear Physics, Vol. 3, Pergamon Press,1981.
Nuclear Momentum and Density Distributions in Nuclei (with A.N. Antonov and I.Zh. Petkov), Oxford, 1988.
Pre-Equilibrium Nuclear Reactions (with E. Gadioli),Oxford, 1991.
Spacetime and Electromagnetism (with J.R. Lucas), Oxford, 1992.
Nucleon Correlations in Nuclei (with A.N. Antonov and I.Zh. Petkov), Springer, 1993.
The Nucleon Optical Potential, World Scientific, 1994.
Introductory Nuclear Physics (with E. Gadioli and E. Gadioli Erba), Oxford, 1997.

Other Books

Nuclear Physics in Peace and War, Burns and Oates, London, 1961.
Our Nuclear Future?, Marshall Pickering, 1983.
Energy and Environment, Bowerdean, London, 1995.
Nuclear Power, Energy and the Environment, Imperial College Press, London, 1999.
Science, Technology and Society, Kinseido, Tokyo, 1999.

THE ROOTS OF
SCIENCE
AND ITS FRUITS

The Christian Origin of Modern Science and
its Impact on Human Society

Peter E. Hodgson

The Saint Austin Press
296, Brockley Road, London, SE4 2RA
MMII

THE SAINT AUSTIN PRESS
296, Brockley Road
London, SE4 2RA

Telephone: +44 (0)20 8692 6009
Facsimile: +44 (0)20 8469 3609

Electronic Mail: books@saintaustin.org
http://www.saintaustin.org

ISBN 1 901157 27 X

Printed by NEWTON Printing Ltd, London, UK   www.newtonprinting.com

PREFACE

The principal theme running through this book is that modern science was made possible by the beliefs about the natural world inherent in Catholic Theology. The conviction expressed in the Old Testament that the world is a rational creation by God was further developed by the teaching of Christ. The debates in the early centuries clarified the nature of Christ and at the same time established the relation between God, man and nature that formed the basis of Christian civilisation. Thus it is no accident that science achieved its only viable birth in the High Middle Ages, when for the first time there was a society permeated by Catholic beliefs. In the following centuries science came to maturity and became a self-sustaining enterprise that has continued to grow until now it affects practically every aspect of our lives, so that they are unlike those in any other civilisation. At a deeper level, it has also changed the way we think about the world and ourselves. Christians have been at the centre of these developments, and have contributed to the debates about the nature of science, its relations with philosophy and theology and the effects of science on human society.

Most of these essays were written for the *Catholic Herald*, and they are supplemented by a number of articles and reviews that appeared in other periodicals. They are so brief that they can only provide glimpses into what are complicated and controversial subjects. Each is self-contained and it is hoped that they will be found useful by people who are too busy to read anything longer and that they will also provide an introduction and stimulus to further reading. There are inevitably some repetitions: if a thing is worth saying at all, it is worth saying more than once.

In Pope John Paul II we are blessed by a man who takes a great and sympathetic interest in science and its many applications. It is therefore appropriate to begin with extracts from some of his many addresses. This concern for science is seldom shown by other members of the Church, but among the exceptions to whom I am particularly grateful I would like to mention Archbishop Josef Zycinski who has provided much support and encouragement over the years, and also to Fr Kevin Reynolds of Sunnyside for his interest in my writings. They have not read this material and of course have no responsibility for it.

P.E. Hodgson,
Corpus Christi College,
Oxford.
October 2000

CONTENTS

MODERN PHYSICS

PHILOSOPHY OF SCIENCE

THE CHURCH AND SCIENCE

SCIENCE AND SOCIETY

PAPAL STATEMENTS ON SCIENCE

INTRODUCTION

Over the years the Popes have provided a series of authoritative addresses on a wide range of subjects that deserve wide publicity and faithful commentary. Thus in recent years the present Pope has strongly supported the activities of the Pontifical Academy of Sciences and has commended scientific research in a wide range of addresses to scientific meetings organised by the Academy. The subjects of papal addresses have included energy and humanity, the nuclei of galaxies, biological experimentation, the protection of the environment, the responsibilities of scientists, the impact of space experimentation on mankind, cosmic rays in interplanetary space, science for peace, chemical reactions and the environment, tropical forests and the conservation of species, science for development, and resources and population. It will be noticed that these subjects range from pure research projects to matters of urgent concern to us all. They provide incisive and critical comments on present policies, and deserve careful study and effective action.

The conclusions of these meetings are highly authoritative and are often used by the Holy See in its contributions to international conferences. Thus some years ago the Holy See based its contribution to a conference organised by the International Atomic Energy Agency on the conclusions of a study week on energy problems that urged that the peaceful applications of atomic energy be extended without delay to all developing countries. More recently, the Holy See has made influential contributions to international conferences on a wide range of pressing medical problems. The problems of the environment have received sustained attention in recent years. This shows that the Papacy is not only concerned with internal ecclesiastical matters, but is constantly addressing world-wide problems of central importance to the lives of people everywhere.

POPE JOHN PAUL II ON SCIENCE

1. THE FREEDOM OF SCIENTIFIC RESEARCH

The search for truth is the task of basic science. The researcher who moves on this first aspect of sciences, feels all the fascination of St Augustine's words "he loves intelligence" and the function that is characteristic of it, to know truth. Pure science is a good, which all people must be able to cultivate in full freedom from all forms of international slavery or intellectual colonialism.

Basic research must be free with regard to political and economic authorities, which must co-operate in its development, without hampering it in its creativity or harnessing it to serve their own purposes. Like any other truth, scientific truth is, in fact, answerable only to itself and to the supreme Truth, God, the creator of man and of all things.

The collaboration between religion and science is to the advantage of both, without violating their respective autonomy in any way. Just as religion demands religious freedom, so science rightly claims freedom of research. The Second Vatican Council, after reaffirming, with the First Vatican Council, the rightful freedom of the arts and of human disciplines in the field of their own principles and their own method, solemnly recognises "the legitimate autonomy of culture and especially of the sciences". On the occasion of this solemn commemoration of Einstein, I would like to confirm again the declarations of the Council on the autonomy of science in its function of research on the truth inscribed in creation by the finger of God.

The Church, filled with admiration for the genius of the great scientist in whom the imprint of the creative spirit is revealed, without intervening in any way with a judgment which it does not fall upon her to pass on the doctrine concerning the great systems of the universe, proposes the latter, however, to the reflection of theologians to discover the harmony existing between scientific truth and revealed truth.

From the Discourse of Pope John Paul II
to the Pontifical Academy of Sciences on 10 November 1979.

2. THE ENVIRONMENT

Greed and poverty affect tropical forests

The topic you have been studying is of immense importance. It is to the undeniable credit of scientists that the value of the biodiversity of tropical ecosystems is coming to be more understood and appreciated. However, the extent of the depletion of the earth's biodiversity is, indeed, a very serious problem. It threatens countless other forms of life. Even the quality of human life, because of its dynamic interaction with other species, is being impoverished. Tropical forests deserve our attention, study and protection. As well as making an essential contribution to the regulation of the earth's climatic conditions, they possess some of the richest varieties of the earth's species, the beauty of which merits our profound aesthetic appreciation. Moreover, some plants and micro-organisms of the forest are capable of synthesising unlimited numbers of complex substances of great potential to the manufacture of medicines and antibiotics. Other plants possess value as sources of food or as a means of genetically improving strains of edible plants.

Unfortunately the rate at which these forests are being destroyed or altered is depleting their biodiversity so quickly that many species may never be catalogued or studied for their possible value to human beings. If an unjustified search for profit is sometimes responsible for deforestation of tropical ecosystems and the loss of their biodiversity, it is also true that a desperate fight against poverty threatens to deplete these important resources of the planet. An intense programme of information and education is needed. In particular your study and research can contribute to fostering an enlightened and urgent moral commitment.

In this way the present ecological crisis will become an occasion for a renewed consciousness of man's place in this world and of his relationship to the environment. The created universe has been given to mankind, not for selfish misuse, but for the glory of God which consists, as St Irenaeus said many centuries ago, in "the living man".

From an Address by Pope John Paul II to UNESCO
and the United Nations, 1990.

3. THE AUTONOMY OF CREATED THINGS

From the very circumstance of their having been created, all things are endowed with their own stability. Truth, goodness, proper laws and order – man must respect these as he isolates them by the appropriate methods of individual sciences or arts.... Indeed whoever labours to penetrate the secrets of reality with a humble and steady mind is even unawares being led by the hand of God, who holds all things in existence....

For without the Creator the creature would not exist. For their part, however, all believers of whatever religion have always heard His revealing voice in the discourse of creatures. For when God is forgotten, the creature itself grows unintelligible.

One must add that the problem of the legitimate autonomy of earthly things is linked up with today's deeply felt problem of ecology, that is the concern for the protection and preservation of the natural environment. The ecological destruction, which always presupposes a form of selfishness opposed to community well-being, arises from an arbitrary – and in the last analysis harmful – use of creatures, whose laws and natural order are violated by ignoring or disregarding the finality immanent in the work of creation. This mode of behaviour derives from a false interpretation of the autonomy of earthly things – man uses these things "without reference to the Creator", to quote the words of the Council – he also does incalculable harm to himself. The solution of the problem of the ecological threat is in strict relationship with the principles of the legitimate autonomy of earthly things – in the final analysis with the truth about creation and about the Creator of the world.

Extract from an Address by Pope John Paul II to a general audience in 1986.

4. BIOLOGICAL EXPERIMENTATION AND THE CARE OF THE EARTH

Modern Biological Experimentation

Science and Wisdom, which in their truest and most varied expressions constitute a most precious heritage of humanity, are *at the service of man.* The Church is called, in her essential vocation, to foster the progress of man, since, as I wrote in my first Encyclical: "...man is the primary route that the Church must travel in fulfilling her mission: *he is the primary and fundamental way for the Church,* the way traced out by Christ Himself." Man is also for you the ultimate term of scientific research, the whole man, spirit and body, even if the immediate object of the sciences that you profess is the body with all its organs and tissues. The human body is not independent of the spirit, just as the spirit is not independent of the body, because of the deep unity and mutual connection that exists between one and the other.

The substantial unity between spirit and body, and indirectly with the cosmos, is so essential that every human activity, even the most spiritual one, is in some way permeated and coloured by the bodily condition: at the same time the body must in turn be directed and guided to its final end by the spirit. There is no doubt that the spiritual activities of the human person proceed from the personal centre of the individual, who is predisposed by the body to which the spirit is substantially united. Hence the great importance, for the life of the spirit, of the sciences that promote the knowledge of corporeal reality and activity.

Consequently, I have no reason to be apprehensive for those *experiments in biology* that are performed by scientists who, like you, have profound respect for the human person, since I am sure that they will contribute to the *integral well-being of man.* On the other hand, I condemn, in the most explicit and formal way, experimental manipulations of the human embryo since the human being, from conception to death, cannot be exploited for any purpose whatsoever, Indeed, as the Second Vatican Council teaches, man is "the only creature on earth God willed for itself". Worthy of esteem is the initiative of those scientists who have expressed their disapproval of experiments that violate human freedom, and I praise those who have endeavoured to establish, with full respect for man's dignity and freedom, guidelines and limits for experiments concerning man.

From an Address by Pope John Paul II to a Study Week in 1982.

For the Christian there is a Moral Commitment to Care for the Earth

Before this panorama of meadows, woods, streams and mountain peaks we all discover afresh the desire to thank God for the wonders that He has made, so that we can transform our admiration into prayer. For these mountains awake in our hearts the sense of the infinite and the desire to raise up our minds to what is sublime. The Author of Beauty Himself created these wonders.

Today's feast has a special message for you forestry workers by reason of the ecological problem that is implied in your work. It is well known how urgent it is to spread awareness that the resources of our planet must be respected. All are involved here because the world that we inhabit reveals ever more clearly its intrinsic unity, so that the problems of its conservation concerns people without distinction. The conservation and the development of woods is fundamental for the maintenance of the natural balances which are indispensable for life. Everyone is obliged to avoid damaging the purity of the environment. Since trees and plant life have an indispensable function with regard to the balance of nature, it is a matter of ever greater importance for mankind that they be protected and respected.

From the Homily of Pope John Paul II
on the feast of St John Gualbert, Patron of Foresters, 1990.

5.   THE EXPLOITATION OF THE ENVIRONMENT THREATENS THE ENTIRE HUMAN RACE

It is in a global and ethical perspective that I address the question of ecology in my message for the 1990 World Day of Peace. This message emphasises the fundamentally moral character of the ecological crisis and its close relationship to the search for genuine and lasting world peace. In calling attention to the ethical principles, which are essential for an adequate and lasting solution to that crisis, I lay particular emphasis on the value and respect for life and for the integrity of the created order.

Since the ecological crisis in fundamentally a moral issue, it requires that all people respond in solidarity to what is a common threat. Uncontrolled exploitation of the natural environment not only menaces the survival of the human race, it also threatens the natural order in which mankind is meant to receive and to hand on God's gift of life with dignity and freedom. Today responsible men and women are increasingly aware that we must pay attention to what the earth and its atmosphere are telling us: namely, that there is an order in the universe which must be respected, and that the human person, endowed with the capability of choosing freely, has a grave responsibility to preserve this order for the well-being of future generations. As you know in the recent message for the World Day of Peace, I called to the attention of every person of goodwill a serious issue – the problems of ecology – recalling that in finding a solution, we must direct the efforts and mobilise the will of citizens. An issue like this cannot be neglected – for it is vital to human survival nor can it be reduced to a merely political problem or issue. It has, in fact, a moral dimension which touches everyone and thus, no one can be indifferent to it.

At this brief time in this century, humanity is called to establish a new relation of attentiveness and respect towards the environment, humanity must protect its delicate balance, keeping in mind the extraordinary possibilities but, also, the formidable threats inherent in certain types of experimentation, scientific research and industrial activity – and that must be done if humanity does not want to threaten its very development or draw from it unimaginable consequences.... Ecological problems enter into everyone's homes, they are discussed in the family circle and people wonder what tomorrow will be like.

We must, therefore, mobilise every effort so that each person assumes his or her own responsibility and creates the basis of a lifestyle of solidarity and brotherhood. All have to commit themselves to the equal distribution of this earth's goods, to respect for the life of the neighbour in trouble or on the fringe, to development of volunteer agencies which today can undertake an important role in the support and co-ordination in these areas. Their free co-operation will be helpful and valuable to all and will lighten among other things your task as public administrators.

Address of Pope John Paul II to the Regional Council of Lazio, 1991.

THEOLOGICAL

6.   MEDITATION*

Those of us who are scientists are privileged to devote our lives to the study of the natural world in all its richness and complexity. We study the whole universe, spread out in space and in time. We study the structure of matter from the atoms and nuclei, mesons and quarks, to the solar system, the galaxy and the clusters of galaxies. Our timescale extends from the fleeting existence of the elementary particles to the time about fifteen billion years ago of the primeval explosion that is presently the limit of science and perhaps the time of the Creation.

We are familiar with the many symmetries of the natural world, in sea shells and crystals, in sunflowers and cacti, and have marvelled at the pictures of snowflakes, all different and yet all symmetrical. The laws of nature are beautiful and automatically produce things that we recognise as beautiful. Einstein rejected ugly theories. He took a God's-eye view of nature, and asked himself how God would have made the world: "I want to know His thoughts, the rest are details," he once remarked.

Modern physics show that as we probe into the depths of matter new and unexpected symmetries are found. Invariance under symmetry transformations implies the conservation laws. The elementary particles of matter are grouped into symmetry classes. Sometimes one member of a group appears to be missing: its properties are predicted and soon it is found experimentally. The conservation of parity, charge conjugation and time-reversal invariance were all in turn found to be broken, but the product of the three is conserved.

The prodigality of creation is almost unbelievable. There are millions of species of plants and animals, and countless billions of billions of individuals. After the rain has fallen on the deserts of Namaqualand the barren plains and hills are soon covered with a carpet of flowers, stretching as far as the eye can see. It is known as God's garden. In truth, all the earth is God's garden. If we disturb the soil, there are billions of insects, and the seas teem with fishes. Why all those insects and fishes? There are billions of galaxies, each with billions of stars, that may well have planets like our

---

* This meditation was given at a Conference on Faith and Science held in Rome, 23rd to 25th May, 2000.

own. Why all those galaxies? We do not know. Who has known the mind of the Lord?

Each one of these plants and animals is an organism of extreme complexity. All the scientists in the world could not make a single ant, or a blade of grass or even a single cell. And yet there are scientists who affirm that the universe is made of structures of such extreme simplicity that they can drop into existence from absolutely nothing. There is nothing left for the Creator to do. One day they will find themselves standing before the Judgement Seat, and hear God asking them, with gentle irony: "Where were you when I laid the foundations of the world? Tell me, since you are so well informed. Who decided the dimensions of it, do you know? Or who stretched the measuring line across it?"

We can easily be overawed by the vastness and complexity of the universe. Yet, with Pascal, we can reflect that it is we who know the vastness and complexity of the universe; the universe itself knows nothing. We know that the universe is precisely designed to produce life. If the fundamental constants of nature had differed very slightly from their present values, life could not have evolved. This is why we can say that it is our universe.

We thank God for such a wonderful world, and for making it so that it is open to our minds. We can, with some difficulty, attain some understanding of its structure and activity. God has not made the world so complicated that scientific knowledge is impossible, nor so simple that we can understand it without effort. In Einstein's words, *Raffiniert ist Herrgott, aber boshaft ist er nicht;* God is subtle but not malicious. More simply, the world does not wear its heart upon its sleeve. If it did, scientific research would not be nearly so much fun.

Let us pray that we always carry out our work with no motive other than to find the truth. We do not care about our reputations or our positions. We treat other scientists as brothers and sisters in a great endeavour, not as stepping stones. We share our knowledge freely, and willingly help others. We prepare our lectures carefully and spend time with our students even though we know that, despite much lip-service to the contrary, it will do little to advance our career.

With knowledge comes responsibility. In our present technological society the integrity of the natural world is threatened by pollution and climate change. It is not easy to see how its integrity can be guarded, or how its riches can be used wisely. The world has no voice of its own. We scientists are the only ones who can speak for the world. In this sense we are the priests of nature, representing the world, fighting for it against the greedy and ruthless who seek only their own ends. Let us pray that we have the courage to proclaim our findings, in the teeth of political pressures, recalling with Newman that it is easier to quarry the granite rock with a razor, or to moor the vessel with a thread of silk, than to contend against those giants, the passion and the pride of man.

In fulfilling these responsibilities, let us remember the limitations of scientific knowledge, so that we are neither complacent nor alarmist. Scientific knowledge is not easily won, and the results have to be expressed precisely if they are not to be misunderstood. There are always areas of uncertainty and the possibility that some vital factor has been overlooked. And yet, despite these qualifications, we often have knowledge sufficient to form the basis of action. It is a condition of our lives that we may have to take vitally-important decisions on the basis of incomplete knowledge. It is easy to say that we should postpone making a decision until we have more knowledge, but this is often the worst decision of all.

Let us pray particularly for our priest-scientists and priest-philosophers of science, who are able to show us our place in the Divine plan. Let us pray for those in authority over them, that they may understand the vital importance of their vocation, and ensure that they have the support and encouragement they need to continue to develop their scientific knowledge, and to lecture and publish their findings.

Let us thank God for giving us a Pope who values scientific knowledge and blesses our endeavours.

Finally, let us pray that God may bless our work, so that we can play our full part in the life of the Church and of all mankind.

7. * THE TRINITY

How long is it since you heard a really gripping sermon on the Trinity? What does the Trinity mean to you personally? Perhaps you remember singing Newman's hymn with the words: "Firmly I believe and truly, God is Three and God is One." Did you stop to think what on earth that means? Does it not say that three is equal to one, and if not, then what? I will not ask when you last read a book on the Trinity!

And yet the Trinity is at the centre of our Faith. Numerous Churches are dedicated to the Most Holy Trinity. There are Colleges named in honour of the Trinity in both Oxford and Cambridge. The Trinity cannot just be ignored as a mathematical absurdity; we must try to understand it as best we can. Ultimately, the Trinity is a mystery of Faith, but we can begin to understand it in several ways.

We know from Revelation that the Trinity is three Persons in one God, the Father, the Son and the Holy Spirit. The Father is God, the Son is God and the Holy Spirit is God, but together they are one God, not three Gods. There is a subtle relationship between them: the Son proceeds from the Father, and the Holy Spirit proceeds from both the Father and the Son.

If we want to understand something difficult, we can often make progress by means of analogies. This means that we compare it with something simpler that we do understand; they are alike in some ways but different in others. For example, if I want to understand the nucleus of the atom I know that since it is extremely complicated I must find a simple way to start. To do this I notice that in some respects the nucleus behaves rather like a little drop of liquid, in other respects like a gas. These models of the nucleus, as they are called, can be developed mathematically and used to predict other types of behaviour. We can then make measurements and see if these predictions are fulfilled. In this way we can gradually build up our knowledge of the nucleus. This is what I have been doing for most of my life.

The Trinity is rather more difficult. St Patrick made a start with the shamrock, which has three leaves in one, but that does not get us very far, since the three leaves are the same. A much richer analogy is provided by a creative activity such as writing a play. This requires first of all an idea (the Father), and then the incarnation of the idea (the Son), that is the way the idea is actually worked out, the writing of the play, the stage directions, the choice of actors and the other practicalities. Whether the play is a success (the Spirit) depends on both the idea being a good one and also on it being worked out effectively. So we see that the Spirit proceeds from both the Father and the Son. This analysis can be applied to a whole range of creative activities, as described in the book *The Mind of the Maker* by Dorothy L. Sayers.

This discussion is important for our relations with the Orthodox Church. They believe that the Holy Spirit proceeds from the Father only, and so do not accept the word *Filioque* ("and the Son") in the Creed. Several influential Orthodox theologians, however, do not think that this is an insuperable obstacle to our re-union because some of the Fathers of the Church that they recognise are willing to accept the expression "from the Father, through the Son".

The attempt to understand the Trinity is thus interesting in itself, throws light on many of our creative activities, and is important for our relations with our Orthodox friends.

8.   THE BIBLE AND SCIENCE*

The relationship between the Bible and science is one of the most sensitive and important questions of modern times. Countless millions of people revere the Bible as God's Revelation, and science enjoys immense prestige as the foundation of our modern civilisation. Very many people, especially among the young, think that, for example, the account of creation in the first chapter of Genesis is inconsistent with the recent scientific discoveries of the evolution of the universe. Faced with this decision, they opt for science and abandon their Faith.

It is therefore necessary to ask if indeed science has disproved parts of the Bible, rendering the whole suspect. How should we interpret the Bible? Must it be interpreted literally, or can it be interpreted in a way consistent with modern science? It is certainly as important not to claim too much as it is to claim too little. If it is interpreted literally according to the superficial meaning of the words it readily runs counter to science, while if it is no more than picturesque imagery we have lost the word of God.

The true meaning of the Bible is what God intends it to mean, and this must be true because God is the author. It is certainly quite unacceptable to say that there can be two or more contradictory truths, those of the Bible and those of science. Thus if a certain question has been definitely settled by scientific investigation, the Bible must be interpreted to respect that truth. The living authority of the Church through the ages existed before the New Testament was written, it gathered together and confirmed the books that comprise the Bible, and it continues to interpret

---

* Review of *The Bible and Science* by Stanley L. Jaki. Christendom Press, 1996.

it authoritatively today. That is why the problems of the Bible and science is much more severe for fundamentalists than it is for Catholics.

A characteristic of scientific statements is that they often have the sharpness of numbers, or are linked to scientific theories that have been confirmed numerically to high accuracy. Thus, since truth is one, if there is any statement in the Bible that can be verified scientifically, either empirically or quantitatively, then the meaning of that statement must follow the scientific truth. This shows at once the absurdity and the danger of taking the Bible as a textbook for science, an activity directly contrary to the true relation. Equal justice must be done both to supernatural Revelation and to the results of scientific investigation.

In his book, Jaki considers two aspects of the relation of the Bible to science: firstly the interests and tendencies of the Bible to the extent that they are related to science, and secondly the possible historical role played by the Bible in sparking the rise of modern science.

It is evident that the world view of the Hebrews that forms the background of the Old Testament is quite different from that of modern science. The Hebrews were hardly interested in giving a consistent account of the relations of the earth and the heavens, and still less were they concerned with scientific investigation. They thought of the earth as a flat disk and the sky as a tent or a hard bowl. Such views were common among other nations at that time, but the Hebrews differed in ascribing the earth not to many gods but to a single God who rules all the forces of nature. God ensures the stability of the earth and the sky, and is directly responsible for all ordinary and extraordinary events, for the wind and the rain as well as for volcanic eruptions and earthquakes. It is all God's doing, and His wisdom is beyond the scrutiny or understanding of men.

God intervenes in natural processes to show his anger, His pleasure or His promises, as when he turned Lot's wife into a pillar of salt, shattered the cedars of Lebanon and set the rainbow in the sky. He stopped the sun and the moon to give Joshua the time to win his battle, and lowered the clouds and wreathed the mountains in smoke to enable David to rout his enemies. He sent the plagues to Egypt and parted the waters of the Red Sea. In the New Testament, the star of Bethlehem and the darkness that covered the land at the Crucifixion provide similar instances. God does what He likes with nature, in contrast to the impersonal, regular world presupposed by science.

The world-view of the Hebrews contrasts unfavourably with the Aristotelian-Ptolemaic geocentrism, which posited a spherical earth surrounded by the sphere of the fixed stars. Within this world view, scientific questions such as the size of the earth and the distance to the sun and the moon could be and were measured, and subsequently the distance of the fixed stars. No such questions could even be asked, let alone answered, by the Hebrews. Furthermore, the author of the book of Job argues that we know much less about nature than God does, which is obviously true, but that we cannot hope to learn much about nature: "He alone stretches out the heavens and treads upon the crests of the sea. He does great things past finding out, marvellous things beyond reckoning." (Job 9:5–10). This hardly encourages scientific study, and indeed may appear perverse when we recall what has subsequently been learned about the physics of storms and clouds.

The Hebrew Bible is mainly about God's unfailingly efficacious actions in history. The references made in the Bible to nature are made to emphasise God's power over the whole world, a world that He alone designed, created and holds in being. It is here that we begin to see the natural theology that is implicit in Biblical teaching. Since God designed the world to be eternal, it must be well-designed. His works are to be trusted, and He is not capricious. The cosmos shows the rationality of a purposeful co-ordination of parts. The works of God show stability, coherence, regularity and permanence. The stability of the world is so taken for granted that it is used as a sign of the stability of God's plan for salvation. The fixity and stability of nature shows the permanence of God's moral laws. Jeremiah's account of God's direct involvement in nature is interpreted as the result of laws that nature must obey. The God of the Bible is infinitely faithful and rationally consistent and creates entities that share these qualities; creation is the imposition of regularity, the enacting of a law. God made the sun, the moon and the stars, and they are fixed forever since God gave them a law which shall not pass away (Ps 148:6); Jeremiah was convinced that we can know with certitude the regularity and stability of nature.

The Hebrew mind was realist, convinced of the mind's ability to go beyond empirical or sensory evidence. Phrases like "God's greatness cannot be measured" reveal a genuinely metaphysical philosophy because it goes beyond the physical, which can always be measured. Realism is thus also implicit in Genesis 1, a primarily religious document that emphasises, by rhetorical repetition, that God is the maker of all. God is cast in the role of a worker to underline the importance of the Sabbath day, but there is no trace of toil in His work: He produced everything by His commands. Awareness of its rhetorical character should have discouraged the various attempts to find a detailed concordance between Genesis 1 and current scientific ideas. Such attempts can only discredit the Bible, as also do those who take the story to be a myth.

The Biblical emphasis of God's love for us prevents us from ascribing the many physical and moral catastrophes to an evil principle, and assures us that nothing can influence any event in heaven or on earth independently of Him. Hence the strong warnings against all fortune-tellers and divines, and especially astrologers. No other ancient nation was wise enough to see this. The Biblical struggle against idolatry and astrology made it possible to see nature as free of capricious forces and thus a proper object for scientific study. Only if nature is free of such forces can it be studied objectively without it being necessary to resort to magic to ensure its co-operation.

The idea of eternal recurrence, of a circular time where everything is repeated again and again without end, is endemic in all ancient cultures, and is a principal reason why science in its modern form never developed in any one of them. This concept of time is radically alien to the notion of Biblical time, which has a beginning and an end. The Bible begins by affirming that "in the beginning God made the heavens and the earth." Linked with this is the idea of an absolute end, the "new heaven and new earth". Between the beginning and the end is God's plan of salvation.

Eternal recurrence breeds the despondency and despair that characterises the literature of ancient China, India, Egypt, Babylon and Greece. Strikingly different is the hope pervading the Bible, the confident expectation that, in spite of all calamities, God's plan will prevail. Although much of the Bible derives from Egypt and Babylon, the vital distinctions are always made. The animism of those cultures treated the world as an organism, capricious and wilful; in stark contrast the Bible has a quite different purpose, namely to emphasise the complete and utter dependence of nature on God. Thus the heavens rejoice and the mountains shout with joy.

The prophets continually emphasise God's faithfulness to his promises. The book of Sirach, written in Alexandria, continues the Biblical tradition in spite of the attractions of Hellenism. God is praised as the creator of nature, and all His work are good. God rewards the righteous and punishes the wicked. Since "the Most High possesses all knowledge and sees from of old all the things that are to come" nature must be fully rational. The power of nature shows forth the wisdom of God. Great is the Lord's majesty, and "only a few of His works have we seen." This contains no science and gives no encouragement to scientific reflections. But then, speaking of God's moderation in dealing with the Egyptians, the Bible adds: "But you have disposed everything according to measure, number and weight" (Wisdom 11:20), a phrase that reverberates down the ages. The lawfulness of nature implied in these words is also to be found in Christ's words on its regularities.

By calling Christ the only-begotten, John implied a fundamental change in the conception of the universe, demoting it from the divine status it held in pantheism to that of a created being, thus making it a proper subject for scientific study. This distinction between God and the universe implies a total dependence of the universe on its Creator, implying creation out of nothing. The universe thus shows a dependence far deeper than that of an ordinary artifact, and this is of decisive significance for the origin of science.

The Bible thus embodies a very special view of the universe and so provided the basis for the eventual rise of modern science. These implications unfolded gradually. Hellenistic culture mixed science with magic and astronomy with astrology, and it is hardly surprising that the Church Fathers saw in this a spiritual threat. Socrates had seen that the mechanistic physics of the Ionians excluded purpose from the world, and to restore purpose he suggested that all material bodies try to achieve what is best for them by seeking their natural place. Thus the world was conceived as a huge organism and venerated as the supreme pantheistic being, and in this perspective science was inevitably still-born. Greek science had lost its creativity by the time of Christ's birth.

The early Christians were too preoccupied with preparing for eternal life to be much interested in science. Their struggle with the Arians and the Gnostics made them clarify the Christian understanding of existence, and this was invaluable as a preparation for science and for a balanced understanding of its relation to the Bible. Irenaeus' insistence that John's words that "through Him all things were made" meant that the whole universe is created out of nothing, a crucial difference from all Greek cosmology.

Arius, eager to facilitate the integration of Christians into the prevailing Hellenistic culture of the Roman world, proposed that Christ is the noblest of God's creations. Only one expression stood in the way, and it was credal, not Biblical: Christ is of the same substance as the Father. Without that phrase, Athanasius might not have prevailed, a consideration that should impress on those for whom the Bible is the sole rule of faith.

None of the protagonists in that crucial battle realised that the arguments of Athanasius contain the view of the universe that made science possible. The universe made by the divine Logos had to be fully rational, admitting no disorder. Totally unacceptable to Arius was the Greek idea that God was not free to create any kind of world provided it is fully ordered and rational, and that God had full domination over the world that he created out of nothing. Orthodox theology emphasised a fully ordered universe and thus provided the conceptual matrix essential for the rise of science.

The implications of this were realised quite early by Philoponus, who argued that celestial and terrestrial matter must obey the same laws, a belief essential for the development of Newtonian physics. He anticipated the essence of inertial motion, contrary to Aristotle and all the philosophers of antiquity. These remarkable innovations are attributable to Philoponus' firm belief in creation in time, that had by then become a Christian belief.

The first chapter of Genesis has always been of central importance for Biblical interpretation. St Augustine laid down the rule that whenever some feature of the world, such as the sphericity of the earth, had been demonstrated by reason, then the Bible must be interpreted accordingly. It is then evident that Genesis 1 is not a brief summary of cosmic evolution but a threefold emphasis that God is the creator of everything that is, in heaven or on earth. The Bible does not teach us scientific truths that we can well find out for ourselves. Augustine further emphasised that we accept the Bible on the authority of the Catholic Church which therefore has authority higher than the Bible and is its authoritative interpreter.

The first sentence in the Bible played a crucial role in the first viable rise of science in the High Middle Ages. John Buridan, a professor at the Sorbonne, rejected Aristotle's teaching on the eternity of the world as contrary to the Christian belief in creation in time. Considering the cause of motion, he proposed that God, when He created things, gave them an impetus that keeps them in motion. He thus formulated what became the concept of momentum and so laid the foundations of the science of motion and hence of all physics. This work of Buridan soon spread through Europe and made possible the discoveries of Galileo and Newton.

The Reformation increased the authority of the Bible at the expense of the authority of the Church. Luther insisted that Genesis 1 be interpreted literally, even if it required belief in absurdities. He ridiculed Copernicus for maintaining that the earth moves round the sun, as this is clearly contrary to Joshua's command to the sun to stand still. Galileo claimed, incorrectly, to have demonstrated the earth's motion, and proceeded to lecture the theologians on the interpretation of Scripture. Quite correctly, he reiterated Augustine's dictum, but this did not prevent his condemnation though not, fortunately for the doctrine of infallibility, by the Pope himself.

The lesson of the Galileo case led the Catholic Church to adopt a cautious attitude to Darwin's evolutionism, which raised serious problems mainly for Protestants who take the Bible as the sole rule of faith. Similarly cautious is the Church's attitude to modern cosmology, despite the enthusiastic advocates of the Big Bang theory as possible evidence for creation.

Thus the Bible, the inspired word of God, has a higher purpose than to teach us science. Nevertheless, in teaching the truths necessary for salvation, it created a set of beliefs about the world that made possible the only viable birth of science in human history. This is a momentous and most instructive story, told in a masterly way by the author of this book.

9.   GENESIS 1 AND SCIENCE*

The first chapter of the book of Genesis is perhaps the most familiar text of the Bible, and also the most fundamental. It describes the creation of the world and all that is in it, including man. It is also the text that has given rise to the most controversy, and it is a perennial source of difficulty, if not scandal. It frequently happens that young people are brought up believing literally in the Biblical story of creation and then, when they read the scientific account, reject the Bible as naive and false.

There are obvious internal inconsistencies if the creation story is read as literal history. Thus the sun was created on the fourth day, whereas light appeared on the first day, and plants, that need the sun's light, on the

---

* Review of *Genesis 1 Through the Ages* by Stanley L. Jaki. Thomas More Press, 1992.

third day. Indeed, the whole idea of creation taking place in a few days is simply ridiculous compared with the millions of years that we know from extensive scientific studies are necessary for the evolution of the universe from the primeval explosion to the present day.

And yet, despite all this, the Biblical account of creation has retained its power down the ages. Have we perhaps failed to recognise just what it is trying to say and how it is saying it? How authentic is it? To whom is it addressed? What does it say and what does it not say? Is it really an historical and scientific account of what actually took place? These and related questions have to be answered before we can read Genesis 1 properly.

The Bible was given to us by the Church, and its infallibility is guaranteed by the infallibility of the Church. It is indeed literally true, but this means that it is true, not in a superficial verbal sense, but in the sense that it is intended by God to be true.

Genesis contains three inter-related themes, concerning God the Creator of all, God the worker and God the Creator of mankind, the summit and purpose of creation. These convey timeless spiritual truths that establish the foundations of our life on earth.

God is the Creator. At a particular instant, the beginning, He created the world, effortlessly, immediately and out of nothing. He is solely responsible for His creation. It is entirely distinct from Him, and is entirely dependent on Him, so that without His conserving power it would immediately lapse into nothingness. Because it is created by God, it is essentially good.

God is a worker, so in describing creation Genesis provides a model for man, that he should work for six days and rest on the seventh. God did not tire or need to create in stages, or to rest, but we have to labour and then must rest.

God is the Creator of mankind. He did not need to create, but did so out of love. He created man in His image and likeness, with the power to love God or to reject Him. He gave man power over all creation, and commanded him to exercise this power responsibly, as a careful steward.

These basic truths are conveyed rhetorically, not historically. To emphasise God's creative power, it is first of all stated that He created heaven and earth, that is everything, and then the main parts of creation are listed, to emphasise that God created everything. He began, like any worker, by creating the light, so that He could see what He was doing.

Then He created the roof of the world, nearer to the heavens, and afterwards the earth with the land and the sea. On the next two days He created the ornaments of the heavens, the sun and the stars, and then the ornaments of the earth, the birds and the fishes. On the sixth day He created man, and the animals that are subject to him, and on the seventh day He rested.

This account emphasises the creative power of God and provides a model for man to follow.

10.   GENESIS AND CONCORDISM

If we read the Bible literally, particularly the book of Genesis, we immediately notice that it seems to disagree with what we know about the evolution of the universe. Thus Genesis describes creation as taking place in six days. If a day is taken in the normal sense, it is clearly contrary to the scientific account of the evolution of the universe from the Big Bang about ten to fifteen billion years ago, followed by the formation of stars and galaxies and the solar system, and then the geological and biological evolution over hundreds of millions of years. Unless one is prepared to accept theological absurdities such as supposing that God created rocks complete with fossils, this implies that the word "day" does not have its usual meaning; perhaps then it can mean some extended cosmological epoch.

This possibility has inspired many efforts over the centuries to establish a concordance between Genesis and our scientific knowledge of the evolution of the universe. The initial command "Let there be light" can be identified with the Big Bang and the following "days" with the stages of cosmological evolution. Many prominent scientists have remarked on the close correspondence between Genesis and scientific findings. Thus Arno Penzias, one of the discoverers of the cosmic background radiation that provided the strongest evidence for the Big Bang, has said that "the best data that we have are exactly what I would have predicted, had I nothing to go on but the five books of Moses, the Psalms, the Bible as a whole." Victor Weisskopf declared that "the Judeo-Christian tradition describes the beginning of the universe in a way that is surprisingly similar to the scientific model."

Such attempts to reconcile Genesis and science have a superficial appeal, but they are fundamentally misleading. Not only do they gloss over many inconsistencies, but more importantly they are based on a fundamental misunderstanding of the purpose of Genesis, which is to teach us truths essential for our salvation, not to provide an historical or scientific account of the evolution of the universe. As Cardinal Baronius once remarked, the purpose of the Bible is to teach us how to go to heaven, not how the heavens go.

The Bible is addressed to people of all ages, with very different cultural background and very different levels of knowledge. To be understood, its meaning had to be expressed in a simple way so that it does not require sophisticated intelligence, let alone modern scientific knowledge, for its understanding. It speaks of the light and the dark, the earth and the sea, the birds and the fishes, the sun and the moon, the wild beasts and the cattle, and finally man and woman. All are described as created by God, and this continual repetition serves to drive the message home.

Although superficially it may appear to be an historical account, to interpret it in this way is to fail to recognise its literary genre. It is enough to recall the contradiction already mentioned to see that it is rhetorical and not historical. The "days" are not our days, or even historical epochs. Still less is it a scientific account, in spite of ingenious attempts to correlate the Genesis account with the latest astronomical theories. Genesis was written to teach us truths necessary for salvation, not scientific knowledge that we can find out by ourselves. Furthermore, any such attempts are always liable to be undermined by further discoveries. The perspective of the Bible is higher than any scientific world view, however sophisticated, and this guarantees its perennial validity.

11. SCIENCE AND THE NICENE CREED

The Council of Nicea in 325 formulated the Creed that we recite every Sunday. Its purpose was to define the most important beliefs of the Catholic Faith and this was vitally necessary because there were many people who believed and taught a wide range of false beliefs. Familiarity has dulled its impact, and it is easy to recite it without attending to its meaning.

All truth is one, at the deepest level, so it is not surprising that the Creed is also vitally important for science. It emphasises several beliefs that are essential for the development of science. At the beginning of the Creed we profess our belief in God the Father Almighty, Creator of heaven and earth (*factorem coeli et terrae*). This is the most basic and fundamental Christian belief, that God made everything, with the implication that it is good and worthy of study. This is contrary to the belief in the eternity of the world that was held by many ancient philosophers like Aristotle. Such beliefs were rejected by the Catholic philosophers of the Middle Ages because they are inconsistent with the belief in creation. It was by thinking about creation that one of them, John Buridan, developed his theory of motion that was so influential for the development of modern science.

We go on to profess our belief in Jesus Christ, the only-begotten Son of God. The word "only-begotten" (*unigenitum*) tells us that Christ shares the same nature as the Father. This is further emphasised by the words "begotten not made, consubstantial with the Father" (*genitum, non factum, consubstantialem Patri*). Christ is of the same substance as the Father, whereas everything in the material universe is made or created. The material universe is created by God and given definite properties, and it is these properties that science tries to discover. This distinction between begetting and making is familiar in our own lives: we beget our children but we make many other things.

In many ancient civilisations it was believed that the world is an emanation or extension of the Godhead. This is known as pantheism, and was one of the beliefs that prevented the rise of science in ancient times. Thus by emphasising the created nature of the world, distinct from the Creator, the Creed helped to prepare the way for the development of modern science.

The Creed also teaches that all creation took place through Christ (*per quem omnia facta sunt*), so that it has a unique origin. This excludes the pagan idea that the world is controlled partly by good spirits and partly by evil spirits and is therefore chaotic and unpredictable. Such a belief would make science impossible, since the very possibility of science rests on the conviction that the world is rational and orderly. Thus once again the teaching of the Creed provides part of the essential basis of modern science.

By His Incarnation, Christ took a human body made of the matter of the world, thus re-emphasising its goodness and ennobling it still further. The Incarnation took place only once, and this immediately destroyed the belief in a cyclic universe that is found in all ancient civilisations. This is the belief that history is cyclic, so that after a long period everything is repeated, and this happens endlessly. This belief is intensely debilitating; if everything has happened before and will happen again, then why bother? It was the unique Incarnation of Christ, re-affirmed in the Creed, that broke this belief, so that now history is seen not as an infinite succession of dreary cycles but as a linear story with a beginning and an end.

12.   A MIRACLE AT LOURDES

Scientists always like to think that we are unbiased, objective observers of nature, ready, in the words of Huxley, to sit down before the facts as a little child. In practice, however, like most people, we have strong beliefs about what can and cannot happen. Many scientists, when they hear reports of a miracle, just brush them aside as absurd. This attitude stems partly from a strong belief in the uniformity of nature and partly, in some cases, from an innate antipathy to religious fables. However, like it or not, miracles do happen.

Alexis Carrel was born in 1873 and studied medicine in Lyons. He soon abandoned his Catholic Faith and became an agnostic. The reports of cures at Lourdes interested him, and he decided to go and see for himself. On 25th May 1902, he boarded a train carrying the sick to Lourdes, and met a twenty-three year old woman, Marie Bailly, who was dying of tubercular peritonitis. Her case was well known in medical circles in Lyons, and was considered inoperable. Both her parents had died of tuberculosis, and she was spitting blood at seventeen. Her condition was so hopeless that she would not be permitted on the train, but somehow she was smuggled in at the last moment. Carrel gave her a morphine injection to keep her alive. He remarked to a friend that if she was cured he would become a monk.

On 28th May, Carrel examined her in the hospital. Her face was pale and emaciated, her arms wasted, her breathing rapid and shallow, her heartbeat very rapid and irregular, her abdomen grossly extended by solid tubercular matter and fluid, and very painful when touched. She had tubercular sores and lesions of the lungs. Against medical advice, she was taken to the Grotto. She was at the point of death. Carrel watched with clinical objectivity as the dying girl was bathed by the waters, as they did not dare to immerse her. At 2.40pm he noticed a change; her skin was rather less ashen, but he put it down to an hallucination. Her breathing became less rapid, and one of the doctors said that she may be about to die. Then he saw that the blanket covering her distended abdomen was gradually flattening out. Her heartbeat became regular, and she said that she felt very well. She drank a cup of milk.

Later in the day, Carrel returned to the hospital to examine the patient. She was sitting up in bed, her face lively and serene, with some colour on her cheeks. Her heartbeat was calm and regular, her breathing normal. She had the flat, slightly concave abdomen of a young undernourished girl. The flesh was soft and flexible, and could be palpated without causing pain. Two days later, she took the train back to Lyons and walked through the streets to the home of her relatives.

Carrel did not know what to think. Either he had made a mistake in diagnosis, or he had seen a miracle. He considered himself just an objective observer, but how could he make sense of what he had seen? He reviewed his diagnosis and knew that he had not been mistaken. He had witnessed a cure, but still could not accept a supernatural explanation.

He accepted the facts that he had observed, regarding them as an inexplicable phenomenon that deserved further scientific study. He thus became unwelcome in the free-thinking and anticlerical medical establishment of Lyons. He migrated to the United States, where he invented the heart pump which made heart bypass surgery possible (that, incidentally, saved my own life in 1998). For this he was awarded the Nobel Prize for Medicine.

Subsequently he wrote a memorable book *Man, the Unknown,* and described his experience in another book *The Voyage to Lourdes,* reprinted by Real View Books in 1994.

Marie Bailly joined the Sisters of Charity and devoted the rest of her life to nursing the sick. Carrel remained an agnostic until, soon after Marie's death at the age of 58, he visited a Trappist monk and was deeply impressed by his holiness. Subsequently he returned to the Catholic Faith and died in 1944 after receiving the Last Sacraments.

13.   A MIRACLE AT FATIMA*

On 13th May 1917 three young shepherd children, Lucia Santos (aged 10) and her two cousins Francisco Marto (8) and Jacinta Marto (7), saw a lady dressed in luminous white near a holm oak tree in the northernmost part of the Cova da Iria, a field near Aljustrel, a hamlet near the village of Fatima in Portugal. The lady told them to recite the Rosary daily and to return on the 13th of the month for the next five months.

On 13th June about 70 people joined them, and on 13th July about two thousand. Each time the lady appeared at noon, accompanied by a sudden breeze, thunder and lightning and a small cloud over the holm oak. In July a luminous globe glided from east to west across the Cova towards the holm oak. On this latter occasion Lucia begged the lady to produce a miracle so that people would believe her message. Alarmed by this outbreak of religiosity, a local official kidnapped the children on 13th August, when the next appearance was expected and put them in the local jail. This enraged the crowd of about 5000 who had gathered on that day, and they forced him to release the children. On 19th August the lady appeared to the children in a nearby grazing area, and promised a miracle on 13th October. On 13th September about ten thousand people went to the Cova da Iria and saw a luminous globe move across the sky from east to west.

In early October there were intense expectations of a miracle on the 13th. A well-known journalist Avelino de Almeida wrote an article that was published on that day saying that the whole fiasco would soon be exposed when the predicted miracle did not occur.

On 13th October about 70,000 people made their way, mostly on foot but some in oxcarts and automobiles, to the Cova da Iria. During the morning there was torrential rain, turning the ground into a sea of mud. At noon the children arrived and the rain suddenly stopped. Lucia told the crowd to look at the sun, and they saw that the clouds had parted to reveal the sun as a silvery grey disc that could be observed directly, like the moon, without damage to the eyes. The sun began to rotate, throwing off shafts of coloured light like a Catherine wheel. Three times it danced and zigzagged towards the earth. The crowd was terrified, thinking that the end of the world had come, and they dropped to their knees in the mud and prayed for mercy. Then after about ten minutes the sun returned to its

---

* Review of *God and the Sun at Fatima* by Stanley L. Jaki. Real View Books, 1999.

normal place and brightness. The same phenomena was also seen by some people in nearby villages.

What on earth are we to make of this story? The Church authorities were wisely sceptical and forbade the priests to go near the Cova da Iria on that day. However, they failed in their duty to establish the facts by making a systematic collection of eyewitness accounts, especially by enlisting the aid of experienced scientists.

Nevertheless there were many recorded accounts, including those immediately published in the national newspapers by journalists like Almeida who had come to the Cova da Iria to see what would happen. These accounts, taken together, are sufficient to establish beyond doubt what the people saw, although careful scientific questioning would probably have revealed more details.

Once the facts are established we can ask what really happened, and whether it was indeed a miracle. Could it have been a collective hallucination? This seems very unlikely because no one expected the promised miracle to involve the sun, and there were thousands of witnesses, some very sceptical, including many in nearby villages. Did the sun really dance? This possibility can be excluded because of the size of the sun and the laws of dynamics. God is indeed all-powerful, but He cannot contradict Himself. Any such motion of the sun would have been observed by astronomical observatories all over the world, and it was not.

We thus conclude that the apparent motion of the sun was a local meteorological phenomenon. Could it have been a very rare but nonetheless purely natural phenomenon? In certain circumstances it is known that very remarkable meteorological phenomena can occur due to the many different forms that can be taken by ice crystals. However what was seen at Fatima does not in the least resemble the known effects attributable to ice crystals. Perhaps some eddies in the atmosphere produced lenses of air of different refractive indices that could enlarge the sun's image. All this is extremely unlikely, but nevertheless it cannot be stated with certainty that we know enough about meteorology to exclude a natural explanation. The Church has never declared the phenomenon to be miraculous, and will probably never do so.

However, the additional fact that this very rare phenomenon took place at a time and place specified three months in advance certainly indicates that it was a miracle.

What is even less well known than the miracle itself is the key importance of Fatima for the history of Europe. Portugal at that time was controlled by an intensely anti-clerical government that had confiscated Church property, closed Catholic schools, banned religious instruction and forced the Patriarch of Lisbon to leave his see. Lenin had earmarked Portugal as the first state to fall under Communist control. With Portugal in Communist hands, Spain would surely follow, and then France and eventually the whole of Europe would become Communist. This was a very real possibility in view of the strength of Communism in Spain and France. The very day after 13th October, there were new elections, and the anti-clerical candidates lost in regions around Fatima. In a few months the people of Portugal turned against the anti-clerical regime, and it was ousted by a coup. If this had not happened, the whole history of Europe might well have been very different.

There is a vast literature on Fatima, but now the whole story has been told in great detail with scientific objectivity and full respect for the essential and established facts.

14. SCIENTISTS AND MIRACLES

Recently it was announced that the Bishop of Lourdes has recognised the "inexplicable cure" of a 51-year old man who had suffered from multiple sclerosis since 1972. The man is Jean-Pierre Bely, a medical worker from Angouleme, who recovered on 9th October 1987 after receiving the Sacrament of the Sick. Medical experts have studied his case for twelve years, by a whole series of physical, neurological and psychiatric tests, to make sure that the cure is genuine.

This news will come as no surprise to anyone familiar with the story of Lourdes and with the extreme care taken by the Church before attributing any cure to supernatural intervention. The reaction of Bertrand Fontaine, a Paris neurologist, is also typical of many scientists and indeed of many other people, on hearing about a miraculous cure. According to the *Daily Telegraph* of 12th February he said that "while spiritual strength can help a patient to overcome a serious illness, it cannot make an infection or a tumour disappear, nor, in the case of multiple sclerosis, can it repair the damage to the medullary sheaths that the disease attacks."

The precise meaning of this statement depends on what is meant by "spiritual strength". If it simply means the spiritual strength of the person concerned, then the statement is acceptable. However, it seems most likely that Dr Fontaine intended to deny the very possibility of a miraculous cure. How can he possibly know that miracles are impossible? Such a belief indeed follows from the regularity of nature, sometimes called the principle of uniformity of nature. This means that the material world always behaves in a regular way; like causes produce like effects.

How do we know that this is true? One way is by observing that it is followed in practice; if it were not, science would be impossible. An observation or measurement must be independent of where and when it was made. This is the method of induction, but it does not amount to a conclusive proof. If a thing happens in a regular way a million times, this shows that it is very likely to happen on the next occasion, but provides no proof that it will. It is not difficult to think of examples. Thus so far I have lived through many days, but I certainly cannot rely on this continuing forever.

Another way of establishing the regularity of nature is theological. God created the world and gave each object its properties. The faithfulness of God to Israel is compared with the reliability of natural phenomena in the book of Jeremiah (31:35). God is the Creator, and guarantees the regularity of phenomena. He created the material word and keeps it in being. Without Him it would lapse into nothingness. But since he has absolute power over nature, He can suspend its laws at will, and this leaves open the possibility of miraculous intervention.

The uniformity of nature is thus very reliable and serves as one of the bases of science. But it is not absolute; exceptions can occur, and these are outside science.

Dr Fontaine's remarks also show a rather cavalier attitude to the integrity and medical expertise of his colleagues. They spend years examining alleged cures before they finally declare them to be inexplicable by medical science. Often they include atheists and agnostics, like Alexis Carrel, who simply record what they see, without trying to give any explanation. This is a true scientific procedure, to look first at the facts, and establish them beyond doubt, before seeking an explanation.

15. SCIENCE AND EASTERN RELIGIONS

In recent years there have been many books on the relationship between Eastern religions, principally Buddhism, Hinduism and Taoism, and modern science, especially elementary particle physics. Some of these, such as Fritjof Capra's book *The Tao of Physics*, have sold millions of copies in many languages. Such books are very popular, especially among young people, and this is the intellectual counterpart of their journeys to the East to seek wisdom at the feet of some guru. In his book, Capra emphasises many parallels between elementary particle physics and Eastern religions: the interactions of elementary particles are compared to the dance of Shiva and the complexity of the formulae of mathematical physics to that of the Hindu scriptures. It would be charitable to call these comparisons far-fetched; one might as well compare the particle motions to the gyrations of a pop singer or the Hindu scriptures to a railway timetable. Such comparisons can impress only those unfamiliar with the precision of modern physics. When physicists talk of energy, they mean a definite quantity that can be measured accurately to give a numerical result. When a mystic speaks of energy he is using the word in its everyday sense, or perhaps in some higher spiritual sense that is even less scientific. Capra also invokes the fuzzy quantum world inherent in the discredited Copenhagen philosophy, and Bohr's ideas about complementarity.

Whatever one thinks of these ideas, it is a fact of history that modern science was not born in the East. India, China and Japan have some of the most impressive civilisations that ever flourished on earth. They lasted for thousands of years, had a sophisticated social structure, great art and architecture, profound philosophies and theologies, quite advanced technologies, but nothing remotely recognisable as modern science. Now one can find in these countries universities and institutes where scientific research is carried out to a very high level, but it has all been imported from the West. Modern science was born not in the East, but in the Middle Ages in Western Europe, where Catholic theology provided the basic beliefs that lie at the foundations of science.

If we look at the beliefs about the material world that are found in eastern religions, we can easily see why science never developed there. The eastern sages, Capra remarks, "are generally not interested in explaining things, but rather in obtaining a direct non-intellectual experience of the unity of all things. This was the attitude of the Buddha who answered all question about life's meaning, the origin of the world, or the nature of nirvana, with a noble silence." Such an attitude is completely opposite to that of the scientist. In Western philosophy, Capra goes on, "logic and reasoning have always been the main tools used to formulate philosophical ideas," whereas in Eastern mysticism "it has always been realised that reality transcends ordinary language, and the sages of the east were not afraid to go beyond logic and common concepts." The first part of this can be accepted, but what is meant by going beyond logic?

The insights or intuitions of the Eastern mystics into scientific questions are either banal and trivial, so vague as to be useless, or wrong, particularly in the sense that they are inimical to the development of modern science. Whatever is of value is found also in the Western mystics, themselves rooted in a rational and objective way of knowing that did indeed lead to the development of modern science.

I do not for a moment intend to criticise eastern religions as such. For millennia they have provided a set of beliefs and a moral code for millions of people, and many of them have reached high levels of sanctity. But to suppose that they have anything to do with the foundation of modern science is simply fantasy.

16.   FREEDOM AND RESTRAINT

There are many people who have new ideas in science and in religion and naturally they want to publicise them by teaching and writing. Some of these ideas may be based on careful research, and others are just wild speculation. If everything was disseminated there would be such a mixture of good and bad ideas that further progress would be practically impossible. There has to be some way of avoiding such chaos.

The results of scientific research are published in established journals, and any scientist is free to submit an article for publication. To ensure that it is worth publishing, the editor of the journal sends the article to two or three referees, who examine its suitability. If it reports experimental work, they check that the measurements have been made properly and the results presented in sufficient detail. Theoretical work must be properly carried out. The results must be new, and advance our understanding of the subject significantly. The whole must be clearly presented, and established results distinguished from speculations. Even if it is a good article, the referee will usually have a list of criticisms and questions that are forwarded to the author, and the article is not accepted until the necessary corrections have been made to the satisfaction of the editor. This process takes some months, but it generally works well and ensures that only worthwhile articles are published. If an article is rejected, the author can always send it to another journal. A scientist who protested that his freedom was being restricted, or that unjust censorship was being exercised would not get very far. The system is not perfect, and occasionally a very original article is not accepted. The task of the referee is hard, and his responsibility is heavy, and he receives no credit, but it is accepted as a duty to the academic community.

This process applies to research articles published in professional journals, but seldom to articles in magazines and the popular press. Responsible editors may ensure that articles are read by other experts, but this is not mandatory. There is thus a much greater likelihood that inaccurate articles may be published.

There is similarly a need to ensure that teaching at all levels is carried out by people who are professionally qualified, and this is done by requiring candidates for a teaching position to submit evidence of professional competence with a list of publications, and to attend an interview.

In the case of religion much more is at stake. A false idea about religion can do more harm than a false scientific statement, and yet in many cases less care is taken to ensure the correctness of what is taught or written. Those who attend Catholic schools, universities and seminaries, who listen to sermons or who read articles in Catholic periodicals and newspapers, have a right to know that all they hear or read is in accord with the teaching of the Church expressed by the Magisterium. It is correspondingly a duty for those responsible for such institutions and periodicals to ensure that this condition is satisfied.

Once again, as in the case of science, some people are unwilling to accept such conditions. The answer is the same: firstly that if you accept a position in a Catholic institution or write for a Catholic periodical the rights of the students and the readers must be respected, and if this condition is not acceptable you remain free to move elsewhere but never to act or write contrary to the truth.

17. SCIENCE AND CREATION*

Science and the scientific mentality are so much a part of the modern world that we are apt to forget that it is a relative newcomer to the scene. The arts, music and painting, sculpture and drama, the skilled crafts, pottery and metalwork have been known to man for thousands of years and are found in all the great civilisations of the past, developed sometimes to an extraordinary degrees of perfection: yet all these civilisations except our own lacked science, and perhaps because of this all ultimately fell into dissolution and decay.

Why was science born in Europe a few hundred years ago? Why not in ancient Babylon, or Egypt, or India, or China? Why not among the Aztecs, the Mayas or the Incas? This is a crucial question, for we all need to understand science, and we can understand such a movement properly only if we understand its origins. If we can understand the birth of science we can perhaps understand the reason for its vitality and its power to transcend barriers of religion, race and culture.

There have been many articles and short studies of this question, but a detailed and systematic study has until now been lacking. This is now provided by Professor Jaki's book. In it, he examines in turn each of the main civilisations of the past and shows how their main beliefs about the world were such as to prevent the emergence of science or to stifle at birth the occasional promising starts made by isolated men of genius.

The necessary presuppositions of science are so much a part of the air we breathe that we easily fail to notice their very special character. These are essentially the belief in the order and rationality of the world, its openness to the human mind and a vigorous confidence that the task of discovering its secrets, though hard, is eminently worth while. These beliefs must be held by the whole community, for science is the work of many minds.

Nothing like this is found in any of the ancient civilisations of the world. Without exception, they were all obsessed by the idea of a cyclic universe in which after a fixed number of years all events would be repeated exactly as before, and so on for ever. Such a view of the universe is immensely debilitating: if we are but actors in a gigantic cosmic treadmill, if all we do has already been done many times before, then there is no

---

* Review of *Science and Creation* by Stanley L. Jaki. Edinburgh: Scottish Academic Press, 1974.

incentive to do more than to allow oneself to be carried along, listless and supine, by the stream of cosmic time.

Into this world of cyclic despair the Judeo-Christian revelation of one omnipotent God, creator of heaven and earth, came like a thunderbolt to shatter the dreary treadmills of cosmic pessimism. Now we have a world with a clear beginning and a definite end; a world of purpose, of freedom, of decision, of achievement. Such a world automatically provides the basic presuppositions, the intellectual atmosphere, into which science could be born, and ultimately was born. Thus we can trace the origins of science back to the Hebrew nomads in the desert, who first learnt to worship the one true God.

The old ideas died hard, and it took many centuries of struggle before the clouds of cyclic pessimism were finally dispelled. The early Christians were not consciously preparing the way for science, but while they were preaching the word of God they were building the outlook on the world into which it could be born. St Basil, fighting the astrologers in the light of the Biblical doctrine of creation, was dissipating an atmosphere inimical to science. St Augustine in his *City of God* was building up a consistent framework that centuries later was to make possible the emergence of a culture with a built-in form of self-sustaining progress.

With the fall of the Roman Empire and the severance between East and West, the Muslim world inherited the riches of classical antiquity but science failed to develop there because of the over-emphasis in the Koran on the inscrutable will of Allah. Nevertheless they preserved and translated the works of the Greeks and these later on formed an essential ingredient of the culture of the Middle Ages.

In the beginning of the medieval period, Adelard of Bath made an important start by emphasising the rationality of the material world, saying that we must always look for a rational natural explanation before invoking the miraculous intervention of God. Later on, More in his *Utopia* articulated for the first time the chief components of the scientific attitude: the judicious criticism of authorities, the realisation of the potentialities of science for social improvement, and the optimistic faith in progress through learning, science and socio-economic planning.

The explosive confidence of the later Middle Ages led to the great voyages of discovery, with Vasco da Gama and Columbus blazing trails to east and west. The Conquistadors found civilisations, untouched by Christianity, still trapped in cyclic pessimism, and the Aztecs and the Incas were defeated in mind and spirit before they felt the swords of Cortez and Pizzaro.

The Renaissance, with its attempted revival of pagan antiquity, was a retrograde interlude, with Ficino's fondness for magic and astrology and belief in a cyclic universe as a symptom. The Neo-Platonists of Ficino's Academy re-imposed the cyclic confines of Greek thought, and sapped the confidence in steady progress that is an essential requirement of science.

This interlude over, the stage was set for the final emergence of science in the seventeenth century through the labours of Galileo, Kepler, Copernicus and Newton, all devout Christians who were convinced that through their labours they were showing forth the Glory of God. From then on it never looked back, in spite of lack of understanding even in the community that gave it birth.

This is a deeply exciting story, brilliantly told by Professor Jaki with his customary monumental industry and scholarship. It is a seminal book that crystallises and clarifies one's whole view of history, that one wants to read and re-read to appreciate the full impact of the story of the origin of science.

In the whole of recorded history two events stand out among all others for their all-pervasive importance: the birth of a child in a manger and the birth of science, and the connection between the two is closer than is commonly supposed.

HISTORICAL

18.   HOW DID SCIENCE BEGIN?

Why did science as we know it today fail to develop in any of the great civilisations of antiquity? Why not in ancient China or India, where there have been people of great learning for thousands of years? Why not in Egypt or in Mexico or Peru? A brilliant start was indeed made in ancient Greece, but the glory faded and it failed to become a self-sustaining enterprise. All these civilisations, and several others, had a well-developed social structure, great skills in the practical arts such as woodwork, metalwork and ceramics, a written language and basic mathematical skills. It might seem that they had all that is necessary for science to begin, but it did not happen. Why this is so, and how science in fact developed in Europe is one of the most interesting historical questions.

As these civilisations had all the material conditions for science, perhaps the reason lies in the way they thought about the world. Are there beliefs about the world that must be held before science can begin? Introspection suggests that the would-be scientist must believe that the world is interesting and that it is worthwhile trying to understand it. For science to be possible, the world must behave in a consistent way, for otherwise what we find out one day would not be true on the next. Thus it must be rational and orderly, but not in the same way as mathematics, for then we would try to find out about it by pure thought. We need to believe that the order in the world is not unique; it could be otherwise, so that to find out how it actually is we must make experiments. These are some of the beliefs it seems must be held before science can begin.

It is generally believed that modern science began during the Renaissance, but the French physicist-historian Pierre Duhem found that there is a continuous development going back much earlier, into the High Middle Ages. At that time the fundamental beliefs were those of Christian theology, and it is notable that these beliefs are just those listed above as necessary for the development of science. They believed that the world is good and therefore worthy of study because it was made by God. The world is orderly because it shares His rationality, but it is not a necessary order. They also believed that we must try to understand the world, and then use our knowledge to improve our conditions of life.

Thus people in the Middle Ages had all the beliefs about the material world that are necessary for science to grow and develop. The most basic science is physics, and the most basic problem in physics is the motion of particles. A philosopher in Paris, John Buridan, was thinking about the motion of projectiles and why they continue to move even after they have left the thrower. The Christian belief in the creation of the world from nothing gave him the idea that in the beginning God gave the projectiles a certain impetus that remained in the projectiles and kept them going. This is the concept that we now know as momentum, and eventually Buridan's idea became Newton's First Law of Motion. Thus we see the detailed connection between the Christian beliefs about the material world and the origin of science.

The ideas of Buridan and his pupil Oresme spread to other universities and were familiar to the Renaissance scientists who finally succeeded in showing how motions could be described mathematically in a consistent way. This culminated in the work of Newton, who combined the rationalism of Descartes with the empiricism of Bacon to develop his theory of motion. With his three laws, together with the principle of gravitational attraction, he showed how terrestrial and celestial motions can be treated in a unified way, and the motions of the moon and the planets calculated to high accuracy. This established science as a self-sustaining enterprise that is still growing today. As we do our scientific work, we can remember the origin of the beliefs on which it is based.

19.   THE FLAT EARTH STORY

A recent letter to the *Catholic Herald* repeated the old story that Galileo said that the earth is round and the Pope said it wasn't, thus providing an example of papal obscurantism. The truth is quite different. The ancient Greeks knew that the earth is round, and the dispute with Galileo concerned the question whether the earth or the sun is at the centre of the solar system.

The ancient Babylonians thought that the earth was flat, and surrounded by oceans, with the dome of the heavens above. Later on the early Greeks, using the knowledge gained by sailors in the Mediterranean, thought that the earth is a disc. Pythagoras the geometer (born about 560 BC) was impressed by numbers and geometrical symmetries, and thought that the surface of the earth is curved. This is supported by the observation that a ship appears to sink below the horizon as it moves away. From that it is a leap of faith to the idea of a spherical earth.

The Greek philosopher Aristotle (born 384 BC) believed that the earth is spherical and stationary at the centre of the universe, with the sun, the planets and the stars revolving around it. Eratosthenes succeeded in finding the radius of the earth by measuring the difference between the altitude of the sun at the same time when viewed from Alexandria and Aswan, and the value he obtained was reasonably accurate. So there is no doubt that the ancients knew that the earth is round, and this knowledge was not lost.

Another Greek, Aristarchus of Samos, together with several others, believed that the earth rotates daily on its axis, and also that it orbits the sun, which is fixed at the centre of the universe. This is called the heliocentric theory. He realised that this raises a serious difficulty, namely that the relative positions of the stars should then appear to change slightly at different times of the year, whereas they always appear in the same relative positions. The only way round this difficulty is to say that the stars are extremely far away; this is in fact correct, but it seemed inconceivable at that time. So most people still believed that the earth is stationary at the centre of the universe. The small changes in the relative positions of the stars were eventually detected, but only by extremely careful measurements made around 1838.

Now what has all this got to do with the Pope? On the basis of many observations made with his new telescope, Galileo found that many of the ideas of Aristotle about the universe are wrong. Thus the celestial realm is not perfect and unchangeable; there are mountains on the moon and spots on the sun. He also had good but not conclusive reasons for believing that the earth is not stationary but orbits the sun. The Aristotelians were very angry about this and made trouble for him by saying that the heliocentric theory is contrary to Scripture: thus Joshua commanded the sun to stand still, which implies that it is normally moving. Galileo replied that Scripture was not written to teach science and uses the expressions of common speech, as we still do when we say that the sun rises in the morning. To quote Cardinal Baronius, Scripture teaches us how to go to heaven, not how the heavens go. Galileo was told by Cardinal Bellarmine that the normal interpretation of Scripture must be followed, but that if ever the heliocentric theory was definitely proved then Scripture must be re-interpreted accordingly. At that time there was no definite proof, so Galileo was told to keep quiet until he could find such a proof. He was unable to do this, and ended in deep trouble. But that is another story.

20. THE RELEVANCE OF PHYSICS*

This book is concerned with the history of physics and the relevance of physics to other disciplines and to human culture. It reviews the whole development of physics through the ages, the central themes of physical research, the relation of physics to biology, metaphysics, ethics and theology, and its influence on recent historical events. In its general comprehensiveness, its accuracy of detail, its sureness of touch in may diverse fields and in its success in building a balanced picture of a vital and influential subject, it is unsurpassed by any other work.

In his account of the history of physics, Jaki distinguishes three phases, when the world was considered to be in turn an organism, a mechanism, and a pattern of numbers. He describes in detail the pioneer work of the Greeks and in particular the work of Aristotle which dominated the scene for more than a millennium. Ultimately this was recognised to be a failure because of its generality and lack of precision: in physics an explanation that explains practically everything in fact explains nothing. The rise of Newtonian mechanistic science in the seventeenth century provided a way of calculating measurable phenomena, and the results were astonishingly accurate, particularly for the motions of the solar system. Fired by this success, men came to entertain wholly exaggerated views of the power of science, and sought to apply its methods in widely different fields, generally with discouraging results. In physics itself by the end of the nineteenth century it became the general view that the grand edifice of physics was essentially complete and that little more remained to be done beyond tidying up a few corners and increasing the accuracy of a few measurements. The early work on radioactivity, the relativity theory of Einstein and the quantum theory of Planck soon altered this, and with the development of quantum mechanics in the 'twenties by Schrödinger and Heisenberg it was realised that no purely mechanical model could be made of atomic and nuclear phenomena. Human imagination can no longer visualise exactly what is going on, and we have to work with abstract

* Review of *The Relevance of Physics* by Stanley L. Jaki. Chicago: University of Chicago Press, 1966.

mathematical symbolism if we aspire to an accurate description of phenomena.

In the second section, on the central themes of physical research, he gives an account of research into the successive layers of matter, the molecular, atomic, nuclear and finally the subnuclear world of the elementary particles. At each level phenomena appeared that pointed to a deeper layer, and the recent work on quarks opens up a still deeper layer. From time to time eminent scientists have expressed their belief in the finality and completeness of contemporary science, but always new depths of complexity have opened up, and forced us to realise the fragmentary and superficial nature of our knowledge. A similar story unfolds on the macroscopic level of astronomy, as man first began to understand the solar system, the galaxy and the systems of galaxies, poised in limitless space. Here perhaps more than in any other field of science the theories and speculations succeed each other with bewildering rapidity. A final chapter considers the vital importance of precision in physics, that insatiable urge to measure more and more accurately that has time and again led to whole new fields of discovery.

Here particularly the author shows his deep understanding of the way research in physics is actually carried out, as distinct from the neat records subsequently prepared for publication. He knows all the false starts, the unsupported hypotheses, the succession of failures that are the daily experience of the working scientist. He describes with many case histories how men and women have gradually groped their way through the fogs of error to define their ideas with ever-increasing precision until finally they are able at length to put in place one more stone in the scientific edifice. This is the human face of science that deserves to be better known as a correction to the all too prevalent myths of scientific advance as linear, logical, coherent, inevitable.

So spectacular have been the successes of physics that it became for many the paradigm of intellectual activity, the only way to knowledge in any field. Inevitably, enthusiasts attempted to apply its methods in practically every field of human thought and endeavour. In biology it led to living organisms being considered essentially as machines, but in spite of a few successes this tended to lead to their most important specific characteristics, their unity of behaviour, their purposefulness and in the case of man his self-consciousness being undervalued. The early estimates by physicists of the age of the earth proved a great embarrassment to geologists and biologists who required much longer periods to account for the history of the earth's crust and for organic evolution, but the difficulty was later removed by the discovery of radioactivity.

The relation between physics and metaphysics has not been a happy one. Metaphysicians have not been slow to lay down the law about physics in a way that could not but evoke ridicule and contempt from physicists, and Jaki gives many illustrations of this. Nevertheless, physics inevitably rests on metaphysical foundations, and it is vital for the physicist to clarify these as far as possible, rather than allowing them to remain a mixture of unconscious prejudices imbibed from a variety of sources. Physics inevitably raises metaphysical questions, and no one but the physicist is able to tackle them with adequate knowledge.

In the eighteenth century there were several attempts, notably by Hobbes and Spinoza, to develop an ethics based on the models of Euclidean geometry and Newtonian mechanics. The rigid determinism of classical physics posed a problem for believers concerning the freedom of the will, and these discussions were further influenced by the probabilistic interpretation of quantum mechanics. On the whole the physicists, notably Kelvin and Planck, were not sympathetic to these applications of physical principles to ethical problems. Nearer our own time, physicists have been forced by the sociological effects of their discoveries, notably in nuclear physics, to examine ethical questions.

The interaction of physics and theology is a particularly long and delicate one, and here Jaki shows a masterly balance in his historical survey. Theologians naturally think within the contemporary scientific view of the world, but do well not to become too committed to it, for it is continually developing with the advance of science. On many theological questions, such as the creation and the end of the world, science has from time to time been thought to throw some light, but the provisional character of scientific conclusions concerning such remote epochs renders such argument extremely uncertain.

The successes of science have even led some to propose it as the basis for the organisation of human society, and Condorcet and Comte were the first to elaborate definite proposals. Unfortunately their knowledge of science and the way it develops was rather limited, and they ended up by freezing scientific research so that it would not upset their social structures. Thus the deification of science leads ultimately to its slavery. This is illustrated even more vividly by the history of science in Soviet Russia where Lenin, building on the work of Engels, at first proclaimed science as the basis of dialectical materialism. Subsequently, scientific work was increasingly hindered by being forced into Lenin's straitjacket, until ultimately the physicists forced a showdown with the dialecticians. Their obvious ability to deliver much-needed goods established their point, and less is now heard of the attempt to subjugate physics to politico-philosophical principles.

The historical events of the last few hundred years have thus shown that attempts to treat science as a god or a slave end in disaster, and we are still trying to establish the real place of science in human society. The influence of science is all-pervasive, and yet very few understand the way scientists work and the status of their conclusions. Great harm is done by the current myths about science, assiduously spread by eager science writers with no first hand knowledge of research, and there remains a great need to correct these erroneous impressions.

The foregoing summary may indicate in a very sketchy way the broad outlines of Jaki's book and some of the problems he reviews. Such a summary cannot convey the wealth of detail, the appositeness of quotation and illustration and the massive scholarship of this work. Here is a man who deeply understands physics from the inside, is profoundly aware of its history, and knows with masterly precision its implications for other fields of human knowledge and its effects on history and culture. He has succeeded in conveying his knowledge to the reader in a way that orders and crystallises our ideas and knowledge, so that henceforth it will be difficult not to look at physics and its history through his eyes.

It is hardly necessary to add that here is a book not only for every physicist to read, but also for every scientist, philosopher, theologian and indeed anyone who cares for the development of our knowledge of the world and the effect of that knowledge on human history and culture.

21.   ARAB SCIENCE

From the eighth to the thirteenth centuries Arab science led the world. The Muslim civilisation inherited the writings of the ancient Greeks and built on their achievements, especially in astronomy, mathematics and medicine. Their empire stretched from Spain to Persia, and they established astronomical observatories in Andalusia, Damascus, Baghdad and Isfahan.

The astronomer al-Bitruji improved the Ptolemaic system and influenced Grosseteste and Albertus Magnus. They measured the positions of the stars and planets, drew maps of the skies and the earth, and invented instruments for determining the positions of ships at sea, and sundials to determine the time for prayer. In mathematics they developed arithmetic, algebra (the name itself has an Arabic origin) geometry and trigonometry. They established a network of hospitals and made important advances in many branches of medicine, especially ophthalmology, of great practical importance in dusty countries.

There was nothing at all comparable in Western Europe and yet, within a few centuries, the Arab science fell into decline and the West surged ahead. In Spain the Muslim and Christian communities were in close contact, and many translations of Greek texts were made from Arabic into Latin, and thence came to the new universities springing up all over Europe. The translations included the works of Plato and Aristotle. Aristotle, in particular, provided a vast intellectual synthesis that dominated European thought for centuries.

This transfer of knowledge was one of the most decisive events in history. The Arabic world had a lead of five hundred years over Western Europe and might well have become the dominant power in the world in the following centuries. Instead, they lost the lead and stagnated intellectually, while modern science was born in the Christian civilisation of the West and has never looked back. Eventually, centuries later, modern scientific knowledge spread from Western Europe all over the world, including the former Arabic empire.

We might well ask how this could have happened. There are probably several contributing factors. One may be found in the structure of society. In the West, the Church fought for the right to govern its internal affairs, especially the appointment of bishops. This led to an important degree of separation between Church and State. Later on, the universities and cities and some of the professions became legal entities and this provided a forum for free discussions of new ideas. In the Arabic world, by contrast, there was less opportunity for individual freedom.

Another possibility is that the theological beliefs affected the ability to do science. Many of the scientists in the Arab world were Nestorian Christians such as ibn Masawagh who headed an institute in Baghdad to translate ancient texts. His pupil Hunayan wrote many medical treatises and translated all the known Greek works into Arabic and Syriac. In

Damascus the Christian physician ibn al-Quff wrote one of the first treatises on surgery.

This is not accidental. Catholic theology teaches that God is both rational and free, so that the universe He created is both orderly and contingent. His freedom implies that it is not a necessary universe that could not be otherwise. It is essential for the development of science to hold these beliefs in creative tension. If we emphasise the rational, we have a necessary universe, and we would not need to undertake experiments to study it. If on the other hand, we emphasise the freedom, then we have a chaotic world and once again science is inhibited. Muslims believe that everything depends immediately on the will of Allah, and this weakens the expectation of rationality in the universe. This may be one of the reasons why science failed to become a self-sustaining enterprise in the Arab world.

22.   CATHOLIC PIONEERS: FIRST, BUT NOW FORGOTTEN

It is very noticeable that in many otherwise excellent non-Catholic books on the relation of religion and science there is little or no mention of Catholic pioneers. The most notable omission concerns the origin of science itself, in the modern sense of the word. The usual story of the history of science is that the Greeks made a brilliant start, but that nothing much happened after that, especially during the Middle Ages, when all thought was suppressed by the authority of the Catholic Church. Then came the Renaissance when the achievements of the Greeks were rediscovered, the shackles of the Middles Ages broken, and modern science could begin.

The real story is quite different. The first universities in Western Europe were founded by the Church in the High Middle Ages from the thirteenth century onwards. They were centres of intense discussion of all known knowledge, greatly stimulated by the translations of the Greek writers as they became available.

For the first time in history, Catholic theology provided just those beliefs about the material world that form the essential basis of science. These are the beliefs that the world is good, rational, orderly and open to the human mind. Science as we know it failed to develop in all the great civilisations of the past because these beliefs were absent.

Physics, the most fundamental science, had been prevented from developing by the ideas of the Greek philosopher Aristotle, but these were gradually corrected by Christian thinkers. Thus the idea that the world is eternal was excluded by the Christian belief in creation, and this led the Parisian philosopher John Buridan to formulate the first law of motion. Buridan's ideas were developed by his pupil Nicholas Oresme, who later became a bishop. They were published throughout Europe and became known to Leonardo da Vinci and the great scientists of the Renaissance. Thus modern science, which indeed came to maturity in the Renaissance, was born in the Catholic Middle Ages.

Subsequently, science developed prodigiously, and many of the pioneers were Catholics. In the nineteenth century the theory of evolution was proposed by Darwin, who concealed his materialist views. Darwin explained evolution as due to natural selection acting on random variations, but he was unable to explain how this happened. Unknown to him, the explanation had been found by the Austrian monk Gregor Mendel, who studied the growth of peas in the garden of his monastery and in the process founded the science of genetics. Yet the work of Mendel is seldom mentioned in popular accounts of evolution.

In the present century our knowledge of the universe has been greatly enlarged by observations with more powerful telescopes. For the first time in history the whole universe has become the object of scientific study. We are familiar with the Big Bang theory, which provides an explanation of the development of the universe from a fiery beginning about fifteen billion years ago. Popular accounts of the Big Bang theory seldom mention that it was first proposed by the Belgian theoretical physicist Georges Lemaître, who was a Catholic priest. He wrote many scientific papers and calculated the evolution of the whole process from the initial singularity. Subsequently he became President of the Pontifical Academy of Sciences.

Mendel and Lemaître were pioneers of science, yet even to mention them would harm the carefully constructed picture of science as a secularist enterprise that has replaced religion. So, although they were first, they are quietly forgotten.

23.   JOHN PHILOPONUS, sixth century

In the early centuries the works of Aristotle were widely known, and he was considered to have said the last word on a wide range of subjects. Up to and including the Middle Ages, philosophers usually taught by expounding the works of Aristotle, sometimes elaborating them in matters of detail. Very few of them radically challenged Aristotle, and one of these was John Philoponus, a Neo-Platonist who lived in Alexandria in the sixth century. He was born a pagan and later became a Christian, and it was his Christian beliefs that led him to make his incisive criticisms of the pagan cosmology of Aristotle. Many of his ideas were far in advance of his time, and he anticipated some of the work of Buridan on the dynamics of motion. Aristotle had many different explanations for different problems, and Philoponus unified them by reference to the creative power of God. Although he challenged many of Aristotle's beliefs, he retained his conceptual framework, and to the end of his life referred to him as the prince of physicists.

The basic problem in dynamics is the motion of projectiles: why does a javelin continue to move forward after it has left the hand of the thrower? Aristotle suggested that the thrower influences the surrounding air so that it carries the javelin forward. This may easily be shown to be implausible, and so Philoponus suggested that a kinetic force is impressed on the body by the thrower, and that this continues to move it forward until dissipated by frictional forces. This is very similar to the later work of John Buridan in Paris in the fourteenth century.

Philoponus' impetus theory was known to the Islamic philosophers of the twelfth century such as Avicenna, but Maier and Sorabji consider that it is unlikely to have been transmitted to the Latin West early enough to influence Buridan. Impetus theory was developed independently in the Middle Ages, generated by the same Christian doctrine of creation. Aristotle's ideas on motion persisted until the High Middle Ages, and were held by Albertus Magnus and by Thomas Aquinas. Buridan went beyond Philoponus by invoking the creative power of God, who put everything in motion and gave it the impetus to continue. For Buridan, impetus was a permanent quantity, so that if there were no contrary forces or resistance the motion would continue forever. He furthermore considered that impetus varies as the velocity of the projectile and its quantity of matter; although not expressed mathematically this is equivalent to the definition of momentum as the product of velocity and mass. Thus the main credit for the development of impetus theory belongs to Buridan.

Philoponus also said, contrary to Aristotle, that all bodies would move in a vacuum with the same speed whatever their weight and that bodies of different weight falling from the same height would reach the ground at about the same time, a statement usually associated with Galileo.

Philoponus is an example of a man who did brilliant work before the social conditions were ripe for its general acceptance. Had they been favourable, modern science might have developed much earlier than it did. He wrote in Greek, and few of his writings were translated into Latin in time to influence the philosophers of the High Middle Ages. He was a monophysite, believing that Christ has only one nature, a doctrine that was condemned by the Council of Chalcedon in 451. Philoponus was also the first to say that Genesis was written for spiritual and not for scientific instruction, a wise statement that was too far in advance of its time to be congenial to contemporary theologians.

24. ST ALBERT THE GREAT, c. 1200–1280

St Albert the Great was proclaimed by Pope Pius XII on 16th December 1941 as "forever the Patron before God of students of the natural sciences".

Albert was probably born sometime around 1200, and died in 1280. In the course of his long life he made major contributions to a wide range of subjects, as well as carrying out arduous duties as Prior Provincial of the Dominican province of Teutonia. For two years he was bishop of Ratisbon, but resigned so as to be able to continue his scholarly work. He has been described as the most influential scientist of the Middle Ages, and was canonised in 1931 by Pope Pius XI and declared a Doctor of the Church.

Albert studied in Padua as a young man and entered the Dominican order in 1223. He made his novitiate in Cologne and from 1228 to 1240 he lectured in several priories in Germany. He studied in Paris from 1242 to 1248 and became a Master of Theology. He was famous as a teacher and again lectured in several German cities. Among his students in Cologne was Thomas Aquinas, called the dumb ox by his fellow students for his quiet taciturnity; Albert recognised his ability and declared that one day the dumb ox will be heard by all the world.

In addition to his teaching, Albert was frequently called upon to resolve ecclesiastical disputes, and this entailed long journeys on foot.

Albert had an encyclopedic knowledge of logic, philosophy, theology and the natural sciences including cosmology and psychology. He was a prolific writer and wrote about seventy books, including about twenty-two on the sciences, mostly in the form of extended commentaries on the works of the Greek philosopher Aristotle. He is one of the few persons in history who excelled in philosophy and theology as well as the natural sciences. He was a keen observer interested in everything in the natural world, the birds and flowers, rocks and minerals, and wrote books summarising all that was known at that time. He wrote on logic, the concept of time, the nature of being and on action at a distance.

Many of his scientific writings took the form of extended paraphrases of the works of Aristotle, to which he made many additions of his own. He also made experiments on animals to verify what he had read and is thus one of the earliest pioneers of the experimental method. He recognised that logic alone is unable to lead to scientific knowledge; it is necessary first of all to make a large number of careful observations and experiments. Albert's writings are generally less well known than those of other contemporary scholastics but they contain much that is of enduring value that is still being uncovered and discussed by philosophers and theologians today.

As a philosopher, Albert faced the most urgent problem of his time, namely the assimilation of the pagan Greek and Arabic learning, then becoming known through new translations, by Western thought and more particularly by Christian theology. He believed that scientific knowledge and philosophical reasoning is good in itself, and must first be understood and then integrated with existing knowledge. He was a great synthesiser rather than an original thinker, and his works contain a detailed and ordered account of the best secular knowledge of the times in the context of the Christian world view.

Such was his fame that he was called Albert the Great even before his death, and it was most appropriate that he should be proclaimed the patron saint of scientists.

25. ROBERT GROSSETESTE, c. 1168–1253

The beginning of the High Middle Ages was a time of intellectual ferment. Schools, generally associated with cathedrals, and universities were being founded all over Europe, and the writings of the ancient Greeks were becoming available in translation. Christian theology was being re-thought using their unfamiliar but powerful concepts. The writings of Augustine and of others like Philoponus were already forming new attitudes to the natural world.

The two characteristics of the Western intellectual tradition that make science possible are insistence on logical coherence and experimental verification. These are already present in a qualitative way among the Greeks, and the vital contribution of the Middle Ages was to refine these conditions into a more effective union. This was done principally by emphasising the quantitative precision that can be attained by using mathematics in the formulation of the theories, and then verifying them not by observation alone, but by precise measurements. This transition was achieved in the twelfth century, principally by Robert Grosseteste (c.1168–1253), who is regarded as the founder of experimental science.

Grosseteste was a widely-read man who made extensive contributions to many areas of human knowledge. He was one of the first Chancellors of the University of Oxford, and did much to establish the nascent university. His work on experimental science owed much to Plato, who taught that the pure forms behind the appearances of things are mathematical in nature, and so if we are to show this our theories must be themselves mathematical, and so the results of our measurements must be expressed in numbers.

Grosseteste elaborated his theory of the scientific method in some detail, though he did not himself carry out many experiments. He recommended the method of analysis and synthesis; namely that the problem is first resolved into its simplest parts and when these are understood the results can be combined to give the explanation of the whole. The observations and experiments may themselves suggest hypotheses and then theories, and these in turn may be verified or disproved by comparison with further observations and measurements.

He first applied his method to the phenomenon of light. He believed that light is the most fundamental form, the first principle of motion, so that the laws of light must lie at the basis of scientific explanation. God created light, and from that all things came. Light itself follows geometrical rules, in the way it is propagated, reflected and refracted, and is the means whereby higher bodies act on lower. Motion is therefore also geometrical. He studied the rainbow and his criticisms of the explanations of Aristotle and Seneca were useful steps along the road to an adequate explanation. For all his emphasis on mathematics, he was clear that mathematical entities have no objective reality; they are simply abstractions from material bodies. Implicit in his work is the insistence on quantitative measurement, and this in turn comes from the Biblical insistence on the rationality of the Creator, who disposed everything in number, weight and measure.

The works of the Greek philosopher Aristotle became available during the Middle Ages, and were widely studied. Robert Grosseteste wrote an explanation of Aristotle's *Posterior Analytics*, a classic of scientific methodology. In the following centuries Albertus Magnus, Buridan and many others carried on his work, and laid the foundations of modern science.

26.   JOHN BURIDAN, c. 1295–1356

Buridan is most widely-known through the story of Buridan's ass. This unfortunate (or perhaps stupid) animal was poised between two equally-large bundles of hay. Since there was no reason why he should choose to eat one rather than the other he remained in the middle and starved. This was intended as an illustration of the principle of sufficient reason, namely that there is a reason for everything that we do. But if the ass is not to starve, it must choose one or the other. Since there is no way of making a rational choice, the only way to solve the problem is by a random process, such a tossing a coin. This problem was already earlier discussed by the Arabic philosopher Ghazali (1058–1111), using the example of a man faced with the choice between two similar dates.

Buridan, however, has a much greater claim to fame, and indeed has been called the founder of modern science. During the Middle Ages it was the philosophers who studied the material world. Buridan (c.1295–1356) taught philosophy in the new University of Paris, serving as Rector in 1328 and in 1340. He was particularly interested in the nature of motion. He thought about how things move and why, for example, does a ball thrown up in the air move along the path it does, and why does it keep on moving after it has left our hand. Motion is the most fundamental problem of physics, and so if science is to begin it must begin here. The Greek philosopher Aristotle had already considered this problem, and thought that all motion requires the continuing action of the mover, and suggested that this is provided by the action of the surrounding air upon the ball.

Aristotle believed that the world is eternal, but Buridan knew from Christian revelation that it was created in time. This led him to consider the beginning of all motion at the creation, and wrote that "God, when He created the world, moved each of the celestial orbs as he pleased, and in moving them He impressed upon them impetuses which moved them without Him having to move them any more except by the method of general influence whereby He concurs as co-agent in all things which take place." Thus if we throw a ball, we give it an impetus that carries it forward after leaving our hand, so that it continues in motion until it is stopped by hitting the ground.

This shows a clear break from the teaching of Aristotle. What Buridan called impetus was later refined into the concept of momentum, and the idea in the above passage became Newton's First Law of Motion. Buridan's works were widely published and his ideas became known throughout Europe, and in particular to Leonardo da Vinci and hence to the scientists of Renaissance times.

The Christian belief in the creation of the world by God also undermined Aristotle's sharp distinction between celestial and terrestrial matter. Since they are both created, why should they be different? Indeed, Buridan illustrated his concept of impetus with reference to the long jump; thus implicitly presupposing that celestial and terrestrial motions are similar. This made it possible for Newton to see that the same force that pulls an apple to the ground also keeps the moon in its orbit. Buridan also worked on optics, anticipating some ideas of modern kinematics. More important was his work on logic; he gave an axiomatic derivation of the laws of deduction.

In the work of Buridan we see in detail how the medieval philosophers, guided by their Christian beliefs, extended and corrected the ideas of the Greeks and in so doing laid the foundations of modern science.

27. NICHOLAS COPERNICUS, 1473–1543

Nicholas Copernicus was born in Torun in Poland in 1473 and studied classics and mathematics at Cracow university, where he became interested in astronomy. Subsequently he went to Bologna to study canon law and to Padua to study medicine. His uncle Lucas Waczenrode was the bishop of Ermland in East Prussia, and in 1501 he secured the election of his nephew to a canonry at the cathedral of Frauenburg. There he was kept busy using his medical skills to help the poor, his mathematical abilities to reform the currency, and his canon law in the administration of the diocese. Although he was a canon, he was never ordained priest.

Through all this activity he retained his interest in astronomy, and in 1513 he built an observatory and studied the motions of the stars and planets. Astronomers at that time relied on the pioneer work of Ptolemy whose theory of planetary motion enabled the motions of the planets to be computed. It was found, however, that new and more accurate observations showed significant differences from those given by Ptolemy. In addition, Copernicus became increasingly dissatisfied with the basis of the whole system, namely the belief that the sun rotates around the earth. Following the speculations of some Greek philosophers, he realised that it is much more satisfactory to assume that the earth moves around the sun. This seemed to him altogether more fitting, and made better sense of many observations.

Copernicus therefore devoted his energies to devising a new theory of the solar system with the sun in the centre and the planets revolving around it. He was concerned that his work would not be well received, not because it seems that the Bible implies a stationary earth, but because he thought many people would reject it as just ridiculous. There seemed to be no direct evidence that the earth moves, and several strong arguments against it.

He therefore collected the writings of every authority who supported his idea and tried to counter the arguments against the earth's motion. The most serious argument is that if the earth moves we would expect the relative positions of the stars to change during the year, which is not observed. Copernicus answered this by saying that the stars are so far away that this effect would not be observed. In this he was correct, although the very small motions that do exist were not detected for another two hundred years.

Other people said that if the earth moves there would be high winds and tides that would destroy everything. This was not so easy to answer as it required an understanding of dynamics that did not exist at that time.

Copernicus first circulated his ideas privately and they were well received by the Pope and some cardinals, one of whom, Cardinal Nicholas von Schonberg, urged him to publish them. So Copernicus wrote his book *On the Revolution of the Heavenly Spheres* and dedicated it to Pope Paul III. The manuscript was sent to Nuremberg to be printed, and this was arranged by Osiander, a Lutheran cleric. He knew that Luther had already heard about Copernicus' ideas and had expressed his strong disapproval, saying "That fool will turn Astronomy upside down. But, as Holy Writ declares, it was the Sun not the Earth which Joshua commanded to stand still." Osiander wanted to avoid difficulties with the Bible and so, without telling Copernicus, he inserted a new preface saying that the theory of Copernicus was simply a calculational scheme and did not say anything about what is really the case. Copernicus only received a copy of his book on his deathbed in 1543, and so was unable to correct this misstatement.

After the book was published, the Protestant reformer Melanchthon wrote a book against Copernicus' theory, but the new idea was well received in England and in Catholic countries. The trouble with the Bible blew up later on.

28.   GIORDANO BRUNO, 1548–1600

Copernicus' book on the solar system, giving arguments in favour of the heliocentric theory, was initially considered to be of interest mainly to astronomers. It provided a new way of calculating the positions of the planets but, according to the preface that was inserted without Copernicus' knowledge, did not claim to be an account of reality.

One of the first to popularise the theory was Giordano Bruno. He was an enthusiastic devotee of the Hermetic magical religion, which derived from mystical Neo-Platonist writings dating from the third century. In Bruno's times they were ascribed to Hermes Trimegistus, a priest of ancient Egypt who lived before the Greek philosophers and who foretold Christianity. This, according to Bruno, was the true religion and the cure for all the evils of the times. He believed in a living earth moving round a divine sun, and followed the Hermetic belief of Ficino that its beneficial influences can be obtained by talismans and incantations. Copernicus he regarded as "only a mathematician", who had not understood the real meaning of his discovery. Bruno had no real scientific knowledge, and defended Copernicanism against the Aristotelians on animist and magical grounds.

As a young man, Bruno joined the Dominican Order, but his views soon alienated him from the Church. He was accused of heresy in 1576, abandoned the Dominican Order and thereafter travelled around Europe lecturing on his cosmological ideas. He wrote many books on subjects such as the magic art of memory, the infinity of the universe and innumerable worlds, magical numerology and universal moral and religious reform, so that he was seen as an advocate of a new philosophy as well as a new ethic and religion.

Bruno was the first to write a book in support of Copernicanism, in a series of five discourses entitled *La Cena de le Ceneri* (The Ash Wednesday Supper), expounding his view that Copernicanism heralded the return of a magical religion. Seldom has such a worthy cause been promoted in so repulsive a manner. Copernicus would have been horrified, and a leading authority on Bruno, Frances Yates, has said that if Copernicus had still been alive, he would have bought up and burned all the copies of Bruno's works that he could find.

Bruno was arrogant and bombastic, and aroused strong opposition wherever he went. When he came to lecture in Oxford he announced himself as "the waker of sleeping souls, tamer of presumptuous and recalcitrant ignorance, proclaimer of a general philanthropy". Jaki has described him as "a soaring poet, an exalted mystic, an ardent pantheist, a born philosopher, a wizard of mnemotechnics, a vitriolic critic, an amateur scientist, a muddled dreamer, a secretive cabbalist, a dabbler in magic, a flamboyant reformer and an amorous rogue".

In 1591 he returned to Italy with the MSS of a book that he intended to dedicate to the Pope. He expected to be welcomed with open arms, and to be invited to lecture in Rome and to reform the Church. However, he still believed that Christ was a magus and that the magical religion of the Egyptians was better than Christianity. It is hardly surprising that as soon as he arrived in Venice he was arrested, imprisoned and finally burned at the stake in 1600.

After a lapse of centuries, Bruno was rediscovered by anti-clericals in Italy and publicised as a martyr for science in general and Copernicanism in particular. He still occupies this role in secularist attacks on the Church.

It is very likely that the way Bruno associated Copernicanism in his lectures and writings with magical and heretical doctrines played a part in discrediting that theory and thus prepared the way for the troubles it encountered later on.

29.   GALILEO THE SCIENTIST, 1564–1642

The story of Galileo and his clash with the Church authorities is such an important episode in the history of science, and raises so many questions about the relation of religion and science that it is worth examining in detail. Here we consider his scientific work; his theological views will be discussed in a subsequent article.

Galileo was born in Pisa in 1564 at a critical time in the history of science. In spite of important advances in dynamics by Buridan, Oresme and others, the prevailing world view was still that of the Greek philosopher Aristotle. Most people still believed that the earth is the centre of the universe, and that the sun, planets and stars revolve around it. Copernicus had already suggested that it would make more sense to put the sun at the centre, with the earth revolving around it, but at that time the arguments were not convincing. It was largely the work of Galileo that established the heliocentric theory of Copernicus.

Galileo's early work was on dynamics, and he easily showed that many of Aristotle's ideas about the motions of projectiles and falling bodies are false. Then he heard about the discovery of a Dutch optician Lippershey who found that if he put two lenses together in a tube it made distant objects appear closer. Galileo immediately realised the importance of this, and soon made telescopes of far better quality. He turned his telescope to the sky and made a series of startling discoveries. He discovered the satellites of the planet Jupiter, which provided a model of the solar system. He observed the mountains on the moon and the spots on the sun, showing that heavenly bodies are not smooth and unchanging as the Aristotelians believed. He gradually became convinced that Copernicus was right, but unfortunately the argument from the tides, which he considered to be the strongest, is incorrect.

He made several telescopes and presented them to princes, knowing that they would ask their Court Astronomers to verify Galileo's work, and wrote a book in the vernacular (instead of the customary Latin) so that everyone could read about it. He became famous and was invited to lecture and demonstrate his telescopes. The Jesuit astronomers at the Collegio Romano soon recognised his work and became strong supporters.

Galileo continued his work on dynamics, and was able to show that bodies of different masses fall at about the same speed. This is contrary to Aristotle, who maintained that a mass of ten pounds would fall ten times as fast as one of one pound. The story that Galileo demonstrated that this is false by dropping two weights from the leaning tower of Pisa is probably apocryphal. He also showed that the distance covered by a falling body is proportional to the square of the time taken.

The Aristotelians were furious. It was absurd, they thought, to think that such trivial experiments could throw doubt on the mighty edifice of Aristotelian physics that had stood for two thousand years. Galileo antagonised them still further by ripping their arguments to shreds and lashing them with his arrogant and scornful tongue. He had to defend himself because he was employed by the Medici Duke and would very likely lose his job if his work was shown to be wrong, but he was hardly tactful in the way he went about it.

Unable to discredit Galileo by scientific arguments, the Aristotelians thought that they might have more success with theological arguments. They pointed out that in the Bible it is said that Joshua commanded the sun to stand still, which implies that normally it is moving. Galileo, who was a devout Catholic, realised that if this argument was accepted there was a serious danger that the Church would condemn the Copernican theory, which would be a disaster since he believed it to be correct. He was therefore drawn into a controversy about the interpretation of the Bible, which eventually led to just the situation that he wanted to avoid. How that happened is another story.

30.   GALILEO THE THEOLOGIAN

In 1611 Galileo was at the height of his fame. He had made astounding discoveries with his telescope, and basked in the favour of Pope and Cardinals. The Aristotelians, however, who formed the scientific establishment of the times, were furious at the way he had demolished many of the central beliefs of Aristotle's physics and thought that the best way to discredit him was by saying that the idea that the earth moved round the sun is heretical. It was easy to support this by appeal to a superficial reading of the Bible, such as the statement that Joshua commanded the sun to stand still.

Galileo was forced to defend himself, and he did so in a letter addressed to the Grand Duchess Christina. In this he explained that the principal purpose of the Bible is to teach us spiritual truths necessary for salvation, and not scientific results that we can find out by ourselves. In doing so it uses everyday speech without endorsing the scientific implications; even now we say that the sun rises and sets without implying that we believe that the sun goes round the earth. In a pithy saying attributed to Cardinal Baronius, the Bible teaches us how to go to heaven, not how the heavens go.

In this Galileo was absolutely correct, but in the aftermath of the Council of Trent the interpretation of the Bible was a very delicate subject, and the current teaching was that the consensus of the Fathers must be followed, and this supported Galileo's opponents.

The leading theologian Cardinal Bellarmine was asked for his views, and he said that the general consensus must be followed unless there was proof to the contrary, in which case the subject must be carefully re-examined. He advised Galileo to proceed gently and to put his views forward as a useful mathematical hypothesis. His opponents forced the issue by asking the Holy Office for a ruling, and in 1616 this was put in the hands of a committee that did not include anyone competent to evaluate the scientific evidence. Inevitably they declared that Galileo's heliocentric views were heretical, and he was told not teach or publish them.

Galileo continued his scientific work and was involved in more controversies. In one of these, on sunspots, he antagonised the influential Jesuits, who until then had been his friends and supporters. Then his friend Cardinal Barberini was elected Pope and showed Galileo many signs of his favour. Galileo thought that this was a good moment to re-state his views, and wrote a book consisting of a dialogue between an Aristotelian and a supporter of the Copernican view. This was approved by the Church censors and published.

The book made the Pope very angry because Galileo had put a favourite argument of his into the mouth of Simplicius, a third character in the dialogue. It was furthermore clear that he had disobeyed the injunction of 1616 not to publish his views, and he was accused of getting the approval of the censors by a trick. He was therefore summoned in 1633 to appear before the Cardinals of the Holy Office. Several of the Cardinals were on his side, and the case against him was not clear-cut. They therefore suggested a compromise: Galileo would be let off with a caution and asked to revise his book. This was overruled by the Pope, and Galileo was forced to recant his views and sentenced to lifelong imprisonment. There is no evidence that he muttered under his breath *"eppur si muove"* (and yet it moves), he was never physically tortured (this was in any case ruled out by his age) and the imprisonment was in his own villa in Arcetri near Florence, which was remarkably lenient for the times. On the way back to Florence he stayed for some time in Siena as the honoured guest of his friend Cardinal Piccolomini. During his last years he continued his scientific studies, and was visited by many friends, and was able to write a book on dynamics.

In 1979 Pope John Paul II admitted that Galileo had suffered unjustly, and praised his religiousness and his views on the relationship between science and religion.

31. THE GALILEO CASE

Everyone has heard about Galileo and the Inquisition, and the story is still used as a stick to beat the Church. We are told that Galileo was a great scientist who destroyed the old Aristotelian cosmos with the earth in the centre and the sun revolving round it, and replaced it by the new cosmos with the sun in the centre. Since this is contrary to the Bible, Galileo was hauled before the Pope and the Inquisition, tortured, forced to recant and thrown into prison for the rest of his life. He is a martyr for science, boldly challenging the medieval Church that had stifled all intellectual work throughout medieval times.

It has long been known that this is a mixture of truth and falsehood. Certainly Galileo was a very great scientist, who made many important astronomical discoveries and put the science of dynamics on a sound mathematical basis. He had to defend himself against jealous rivals, but had a sharp pen and caustic wit and made many enemies. They attacked him by saying that his ideas are contrary to the Bible, and thus embroiled him with the theologians. Galileo defended himself with his customary verve, saying that the Bible is not there to teach us science. This did not endear him to the theologians, who do not like being lectured on theology by a layman.

Ironically, Galileo's views on the interpretation of the Bible are essentially correct, whereas his science was faulty in an important respect. Cardinal Bellarmine had told him that if the heliocentric theory was proved correct, then theologians would have to think again about the interpretation of the Bible, but he did not say what constitutes a proof. Galileo was over-confident because he thought that he had a proof in the motions of the tides, but in this he was mistaken. Bellarmine was thus justified in asking Galileo to cool things and treat his ideas as an hypothesis.

Nevertheless, it was a great mistake on the part of the Church to declare a scientific theory to be heretical. Galileo then brought trouble on himself by disobeying the admonition not to teach his theory, and made things even worse by publishing a book and putting the Pope's favourite argument in the mouth of Simplicius. Even then many cardinals and other influential Churchmen were on Galileo's side, and by the harsh standards of the times he was treated with great leniency during his trial. He lived in the house of the Chief Prosecutor, was never physically tortured, and afterward was confined to his own villa near Florence.

Despite these extenuating circumstances, it was wrong of the Church to act in this way, and Galileo has now been fully rehabilitated by the present Pope.

Reflecting on the Galileo case, Newman realised that in the long run it would prove beneficial to the Church. The lesson has been learned and such a mistake could never occur again: "For that past controversy and its issue have taught me beyond all mistake that men of the greatest theological knowledge may firmly believe that scientific conclusions are contrary to the word of God when they are not so, and pronounce that to be heresy which is truth. It has taught me that Scripture is not inspired to convey mere secular knowledge, whether about the heavens or the earth or the race of men; and that I need not fear for Revelation, whatever truths may be brought to light by means of observation and experience out of the world of phenomena which environ us."

Galileo was forced to deny that the earth moves, but eventually it was found that this idea is harmless from the religious point of view, showing that we have little to fear from the free exercise of reason, and how injurious it is for religious men to suppose otherwise, for "Nature and Revelation are nothing but two separate communications from the same infinite Truth."

32.   ISAAC NEWTON, 1642–1727

In any discussion among scientists there is no disagreement about who was the greatest of all. It was Newton who combined the empiricism of Bacon and the rationalism of Descartes to lay the foundations of dynamics, and thus of all physics. After a slow growth through the Middle Ages, modern science came to maturity at the hands of Newton. He formulated his three laws of motion and these, together with his law of gravitational attraction, made it possible to calculate the motions of the moon and the planets, and to derive Kepler's three laws of planetary motion. The mathematics needed to do this was not available, so he also invented the differential and integral calculus. For the first time in history it was possible to derive a vast range of phenomena from a few differential equations.

Newton gave a full account of his work in the most famous scientific book, the *Principia*. Very few scientists have read this book, and few would be able to do so. A very distinguished theoretical physicist, the Indian Chandrasekhar, has recently worked though it deriving Newton's results using modern notation, and he says that it is almost unbelievable that one man could have written such a book in just eighteen months.

Underlying Newton's achievement are very precise notions of space and time, and it is notable that these derive from his theological beliefs. He took a God's eye view of the world and saw space and time as the sensorium of God: "Does it not appear from phenomena that there is a Being incorporeal, living, intelligent, omnipresent, who in infinite space, as it were His Sensory, sees the things intimately, and comprehends then wholly by their immediate presence to Himself... He is omnipresent and eternal and so all space and time is equally present to Him."

Within this perspective, Newton defined space and time: "Absolute space in its own nature, without relation to anything external, remains always similar and immoveable... Absolute, true and mathematical time, of itself, and from its own nature, flows equably without relation to anything external, and by another name is called duration."

He recognised the difficulty of actually detecting absolute space and time, and so he also defined the relative space and time that we use in practice. It is generally believed that Einstein disproved the existence of absolute space and time, but this is not so. Einstein formulated his theory of relativity using relative space and time, but this leaves open the possibility of finding a way to determine absolute space and time. This has indeed now been done: absolute space may be defined by the cosmic microwave background radiation, and absolute time by the time elapsed from the Big Bang.

Newton thought deeply about the nature of space and time, and made it clear that they are not absolute in themselves, but only as emanative effects of God. Space and time are in no way part of God, but God's being implies infinite space and time. They are uncreated and co-existent with God and yet dependent on Him for their being.

Newton explicitly mentioned God in the first edition of his great work, the *Principia*, and on 10th December 1692 he wrote to Richard Bentley: "When I wrote my Treatise about our System, I had an Eye upon such principles as might work with considering Men, for a Belief of a Deity, and nothing can rejoice me more than to find it useful for that purpose."

Newton had a great and continuing interest in theology, and spent much time in composing commentaries on the Bible. His views were somewhat heterodox, and he was careful to conceal them so as to avoid trouble. It nevertheless remains true that his theistic beliefs were fundamental to the way he thought about the world, and these made it possible for him to formulate the first fully-fledged scientific theory in mathematical terms.

33.   NIELS STENSEN, 1638–1686
SCIENTIST, BISHOP AND SAINT

Niels Stensen was born in Copenhagen in 1638 and was brought up as a Lutheran. At the age of eighteen he was enrolled as a medical student at the University of Copenhagen and was tutored by the anatomist Thomas Bartholin. He kept a detailed diary of his thoughts and so we know that he took a severely critical view of contemporary medicine: "Actually we learn words which certainly sound good but which don't mean anything. So one should come to recognise the doctor as a man who has learnt the art of saying with puckered brow significant words without meaning." He reacted against the tradition of learning only from books without looking at the natural world, remarking that "One sins against the majesty of God if one refuses to look at nature's own work and if one is content with merely reading what someone else has written about it."

He studied the latest medical publications and made his own observations and experiments. Once he dissected a sheep's head and found a duct leading from the ear saliva gland that had not been previously described. He found the same duct in dogs and also in human beings; it is now known as Stensen's duct. The professor of medicine, Gerard Blaes, dismissed this discovery, but when it was confirmed he claimed it as his own. This led to a tiresome controversy.

In 1660 Stensen went to the University of Leiden to continue his medical studies and made many more discoveries, particularly concerning glands. He found that the knowledge of the ancients in this area was "both very feeble and limited". During his last year in Leiden he studied the heart and soon dismissed as nonsense the philosophical theories about the heart being the centre of the soul, declaring that the heart is a muscle and nothing else. He also developed an interest in geology, and studied the philosophical works of Descartes and Spinoza. He was awarded the degree of Doctor of Medicine in 1664.

In the same year he travelled to Paris and demonstrated his discoveries by daily dissections. He was welcomed in Tuscany by the Grand Duke, Ferdinand II de Medici, a patron of Galileo, and visited the Jesuits at the Collegium Romanum. In 1666 he was in Leghorn and saw the annual Corpus Christi procession and was impressed by the devotion of the people; this forced him to consider the question of the presence of Christ in the world. Not long after he was received into the Catholic Church.

In Florence he began by teaching medicine, and subsequently studied embryology, palaeontology, geology and mineralogy. He made frequent expeditions into the Tuscan countryside for his research on palaeontology, and published a book on the subject in 1669. This work makes him one of the founders of geology, palaeontology and crystallography. He continued his research for several years, making extensive travels around Europe.

In 1674 he decided to become a priest and was ordained the following year. Two years later, the Pope appointed him Vicar Apostolic for Hannover, and he was consecrated Bishop. He led a life of poverty, selling his episcopal cross and ring and giving away his possessions to help the poor, thus irritating several German Prince-Bishops who lived in great style. He worked tirelessly for his scattered flock, travelling around the large area for which he was responsible. He dressed as a poor man in a worn old coat and fasted every weekday until sunset, when he had some thin soup. He became pale and thin, but radiated inner joy. He died in 1686 at the age of forty-eight and was beatified by Pope John Paul II in 1988.

34. ROGER BOSCOVICH, S.J., F.R.S., 1711–1787

There have been, and still are, many Jesuits who have devoted their lives to scientific research. They are responsible for the Vatican Observatory at Castel Gandolfo near Rome which is still a centre for astronomical research. The Jesuit astronomers of today are the heirs to a long tradition, and among the Jesuit scientists of the past one of the most distinguished is Roger Boscovich. He was born in Dubrovnik (then called Ragusa) in 1711, entered the Society of Jesus at the age of fourteen, and studied for the priesthood at the Jesuit College in Rome. From 1740 to 1759 he was Professor of Mathematics at the College, and thereafter worked in France and Italy. He visited England in 1760, and was elected a Fellow of the Royal Society.

During his scientific career, Boscovich made important contributions to mathematics, astronomy, physics and geodesy, and also to architecture and land-reclamation. He strongly supported Newton's theory of gravitation and did much to ensure its acceptance by continental scientists. His most important work is his *Theoria Philosophiae Naturalis* published in 1758. The central idea of this work is to explain all the properties of matter in terms of a single law of force, a theory that differs in several respects from the atomism current at that time. It was generally believed that matter consists of small atoms of different shapes that combine in different ways by gravitational attraction to give the observed properties.

Boscovich, on the other hand, proposed that matter is composed of identical point particles interacting through fields of force. These fields vary with the distance from each particle in a way that gives the properties of matter: near the particle, the field is repulsive, to prevent all matter collapsing onto itself. Further away, the force becomes attractive and eventually coincides with Newton's law of gravitational attraction. Although it was entirely qualitative, these ideas were a brilliant anticipation of modern theories of the nuclear forces. The nucleon-nucleon forces are repulsive at small distances, preventing nuclear collapse. The change from repulsive to attractive implies a position of equilibrium, so that all nuclei have almost constant density. Applied to atoms, these ideas make possible the existence of stable configurations such as the electronic orbits in the atom, and of molecules composed of several atoms, held together by forces now called van der Waals forces. Boscovich's emphasis on fields of force was thus an important forerunner of the advances in field theory that took place in the nineteenth century, particularly through Maxwell's theory of the electromagnetic field.

In the course of this work Boscovich raised a number of fundamental questions convening the properties of matter, such as whether the lengths of objects are invariant, how can atoms join together in stable groups and whether the mass of a system is invariant. He was wrestling with questions that were not destined to become of central importance for another 150 years. Thus he has been called "a 20th-century mind in the 18th century". His works were widely studied, particularly by famous scientists such as Michael Faraday, Sir William Hamilton, James Clerk Maxwell and Lord Kelvin, and undoubtedly influenced their own work.

Boscovich wrote several books on mathematics and astronomy, dealing with spherical trigonometry, the cycloid, conic sections, the accuracy of astronomical observations, the rotation of the sun, the orbits of planets and comets, the aurora borealis, the shape of the earth, gravity and several optical problems. In addition to this fundamental work, Boscovich was appointed by Pope Benedict XIV to advise on the cracks found in the dome of St Peter's and to measure an arc of the meridian through Rome.

35.   NAPOLEON AND LAPLACE, 1749–1827

The story of the encounter between Laplace and Napoleon is part of the folk-lore of science, symbolising the rejection of religion by the new scientific community. Pierre Laplace, sometimes called the French Newton, was one of the greatest of the mathematical physicists who developed Newton's dynamics and used it to calculate the motions of the moon and the planets to the highest accuracy and found that they were in agreement with the extremely accurate observations that were by then available. One day, so the story goes, he presented Napoleon with a copy of his magisterial *Traité de Mécanique Céleste* (Treatise on Celestial Mechanics), a comprehensive analysis of the motions of the planets, showing how they conform accurately to Newton's laws. Napoleon looked at the book, and remarked that "Newton in his works speaks of God. I have gone through yours, but find no mention of God." Laplace is said to have replied: "I found no need for that hypothesis." This story is still recounted with relish by secularists intent on relegating belief in God to the status of a discarded hypothesis.

It is however rather improbable that Laplace would have spoken in this way to the all-powerful ruler of France, who was indeed no friend of atheism. When Laplace learned that the story was to be included in an account of his life, he demanded that it be omitted: he did not want to be represented as an atheist.

Even if it were true, the story does not bear the weight put on it. In his analysis of the motions of the planets, Newton was concerned about the stability of their motions against small perturbations, such as those that come from the attractions of the other planets. He therefore postulated that every now and then God intervenes to keep the planets on the right track. This suggestion had the additional advantage that it kept God in the picture, whereas on a purely mechanistic view it seems that there is little left for Him to do. Laplace however, in his very detailed studies of the motions of the planets, proved that their motions are in fact stable against the small perturbations due to the other planets, and so there is no need to invoke God's intervention to keep them in their orbits. That is the reason why he had no need for that hypothesis. Christians unwise enough to use Newton's suggestion as an argument for the Deity were then discomforted, and secularists given another story to add to their propaganda. It is the task of scientists to solve problems by scientific means, and not to invoke God's power to get them out of their difficulties.

In his writings Laplace showed the influence of the prevailing materialist philosophy of the eighteenth century, but he never considered himself to be a materialist. His friend Dumas, the chemist, remarked that Laplace gave materialists their most specious arguments, without sharing their convictions. When he came to die he reaffirmed his Catholic Faith, and the newspaper report of his death recorded that he died in the arms of two priests, who had given him the Last Sacraments of the Church, so he is hardly suitable to be a hero of secularism.

This is fully documented in *Christianity and the Leaders of Modern Science* by Karl A. Kneller, originally published in 1911 and recently reprinted by Real View Books. This book contains very detailed biographies of a large number of the most distinguished scientists and mathematicians of the nineteenth century including, to name but a few, Euler, Gauss, Cauchy, Riemann, Rumford, Davy, Herschel, Leverrier, Volta, Ampère, Faraday, Galvani, Maxwell, Fizeau, Foucault, Biot, Brewster, Stokes, Kelvin, Dumas, Haüy, Cuvier and Bernard, who were either profoundly religious or openly professed the Christian Faith.

36.   EDWARD HOWARD, 1774–1816

It is rather unusual for a member of an aristocratic family to become a scientist, but that was the decision of Edward Howard, the younger brother of the 12th Duke of Norfolk. Younger sons of the peerage, who inherit neither titles nor estates, usually choose the Armed Services, the law or the Church. All these possibilities were open to the young Howard. At the age of nine he went to the English College at Douai for his schooling. His ancestor Cardinal Philip Howard (1629–1695) was associated with the College in its early days, and many young Howards were subsequently educated there. The curriculum was predominantly classical, with rather little mathematics or science. There is little information concerning his scientific education, but by his mid-twenties he was already recognised as a chemist of great ability.

His first major discovery was the highly explosive mercury fulminate, and he described its properties and method of preparation in a series of papers. The research was highly dangerous, and he nearly lost his life when a thick glass vessel was a shattered in an explosion. The substance was found to explode more violently than gunpowder, but it did so very rapidly and so was not useful for propelling projectiles, as this requires a steady and sustained explosion. During tests at Woolwich several guns were burst apart by the violence of the explosion. After a second explosion in his laboratory Howard stopped his work on the fulminates. It was 174 years before the reaction and the structure of the fulminates were fully understood. They eventually found application as very efficient detonators and were used exclusively in rifle and artillery ammunition for about eighty years until they were superseded by a more powerful chemical in the nineteen twenties.

After his work on the fulminates, Howard turned his attention to meteorites. It was some time before the existence of meteorites was recognised by the scientific community, and nothing was known about their origin. Howard carefully analysed several meteorites, and found that they contain appreciable quantities of nickel, together with silica and many other substances which he identified and recorded. He suspected that they have a cosmic origin, as was subsequently found to be the case, but cautiously confined himself to reporting the results of his analyses.

He then studied a more practical problem, the refining of sugar. In the early nineteenth century this was done in small factories, over fifty in London alone. The raw sugar was imported as crude Muscovado, a brown sticky substance containing sugar, syrup, cane fibres, earth and dirt. This was dissolved in hot water, and the resulting liquid clarified by the addition of lime, egg white and bull's blood. The clear portion was separated and evaporated in large shallow pans. The whole process was crude, wasteful and dangerous. The factories were usually wooden buildings that easily caught fire. Howard showed considerable ability by inventing and designing a closed vacuum vessel that enabled the sugar to be evaporated under reduced pressure. This proved much safer and more efficient as it reduced the danger of fire and the amount of sugar decomposed. His method was very successful and replaced the older ones.

Howard was indifferent to scientific renown, free from professional jealousy and kept himself aloof from controversy. He was content to carry out pioneer investigations, leaving it to others to fill in the details and to work out the practical applications. He died quite young and is now largely forgotten, but he made important advances that had widespread consequences. His grandson was Cardinal Edward Henry Howard (1829–1892).

37. JOHN HENRY NEWMAN, 1801–1890

John Henry Newman is best known as a profound spiritual writer, and also as a master of English prose and the author of *The Dream of Gerontius*. What is much less well known is his keen interest in the science of his times, and the contemporary debates on the relation between religion and science. When he was an undergraduate at Oxford, he read for Honours in both classics and mathematics. He arrived so well prepared in mathematics that his tutor Mr Short urged him to sit for the Trinity Scholarship; he did so and was successful. For his final examination he studied geometry, algebra and trigonometry, Newton's *Principia*, hydrostatics, astronomy, mechanics and optics. Subsequently he attended lectures in anatomy, geology and mineralogy. When he stood for the Oriel fellowship he confided to his father that "few have attained the facility and comprehension which I have arrived at from the regularity and constancy of my reading and the laborious and nerve-bracing and fancy-repressing study of mathematics, which has been my principal subject."

Subsequently, as a Fellow of Oriel, he helped the Provost, Dr Whately, to write his article on logic. These thorough studies of mathematics, logic and physics certainly contributed to the formation of his mind, and account for the clarity and cogency of his writings.

Many years later, he was invited to become Rector of the proposed new university in Ireland. When he arrived in Dublin, he sought to gain support by a series of discourses on the nature and scope of university education, later published as *The Idea of a University*. The curriculum of the university included mathematics, physics, chemistry, natural history, mineralogy and geology. A School of Medicine was established, and this was followed by a School of Engineering. He wanted to set up astronomical and meteorological observatories, but was unable to do so for lack of funds.

Newman regarded a university as primarily a teaching institution, but he also wanted his professors to undertake some research. He also planned a school of useful arts, so that the schools of engineering, mining and agriculture could develop and apply the natural resources of Ireland.

In his lectures in Dublin, and in many subsequent writings, Newman explored the relation between theology and the natural sciences. On the one hand, he had to counter the prevailing materialistic view that scientific knowledge alone is worth having, while on the other he had to avoid making science so subservient to theology that its natural growth would be made impossible. Theology and science have different subject matters, and to some extent different methods, but nevertheless they are related to each other.

In his book on a *Grammar of Assent*, Newman explored the ways we come to believe, and found instructive similarities between theology and science, and indeed everyday beliefs as well. We rarely believe because of a logical demonstration, but much more frequently by the convergence of probabilities. This is the case in our everyday affairs, and also in science and in religion. It is indeed fitting that our beliefs should engage the whole person and not just our minds, for "man is *not* a reasoning animal; he is a seeing, feeling contemplating, active animal."

Darwin's theory of evolution caused much confusion, particularly to those who believed in the literal surface meaning of the Bible. Newman found it much more plausible that God created matter long ages ago with properties that ensured that it evolved into what we see today. Thus he believed that evolution is much more plausible than special creation a few thousand years ago, and rejected the idea that God created rocks with fossils in them.

38.   THE WILBERFORCE-HUXLEY DEBATE

A famous example of conflict between science and religion is the debate between Samuel Wilberforce, the Anglican Bishop of Oxford (known as Soapy Sam), and the biologist T.H. Huxley at a meeting of the British Association in Oxford on 30th June 1860. According to the usual story, Wilberforce poured scorn on Darwin's *Origin of Species* and was vanquished by Huxley, whose scientific sincerity humbled the insolence and obscurantism of Soapy Sam. Thus the pretension of the Church to dictate to scientists what conclusions they could reach was decisively defeated and the autonomy of science affirmed.

The encounter is described (38 years later) in the October 1898 issue of *Macmillan's Magazine:* "I was happy enough to be present on the memorable occasion at Oxford when Mr Huxley bearded Bishop Wilberforce. There were so many of us that were eager to hear that we had to adjourn to the great library of the Museum. I can still hear the American accents of Dr Draper's opening address, when he asked 'Air we a fortuitous concourse of atoms?'. Then the bishop rose, and in a light scoffing tone, florid and fluent, he assured us that there was nothing in the idea of evolution: rock pigeons were what rock pigeons had always been. Then, turning to his antagonist with a smiling insolence, he begged to know, was it through his grandfather or his grandmother that he claimed descent from a monkey? On this Mr Huxley slowly and deliberately arose. A slight tall figure stern and pale, very quiet and very grave, he stood before us, and spoke those tremendous words – words which no one seems sure of now, nor I think, could remember just after they had been spoken for their meaning took away our breath, though it left in no doubt as to what it was. He was not ashamed to have a monkey for an ancestor; but he would be ashamed to be connected with a man who used great gifts to obscure the truth. No one doubted his meaning and the effect was tremendous."

The few contemporary accounts tell rather a different story. There are two reports of journalists who were actually present, and neither reported the "tremendous words" of Huxley. In a letter he wrote to Darwin the next day, Hooker made no mention of them.

There was certainly a vigorous debate. Interest in Darwin's ideas was high, and the Bishop of Oxford had strongly opposed the idea that men may be descended from apes. He was supported by many distinguished scientists including Professor Owen and Sir Benjamin Brodie. Darwin could not come because of illness, so it fell to Huxley to defend Darwin's views. Wilberforce had already written a review of Darwin's *Origin of Species* that was mainly devoted to a scientific assessment of the theory. He made clear that its truth should be judged objectively, and emphasised that he had "no sympathy with those who object to any facts or alleged facts in nature, or an inference logically deduced from them, because they believe them to contradict what it appears to them is taught by Revelation. We think that all such objections savour of a timidity which is really inconsistent with a firm and well-trusted faith." It is thus very difficult to cast Wilberforce as an authoritarian cleric trying to throw doubt on genuine scientific observations.

At that time there were many serious objections to evolution, and most scientists were sceptical. Evolution cannot be proved, and in 1860 it was quite reasonable to point to the gaps in the theory and to argue that Darwin's idea was a conjecture and not a well-supported theory. Nevertheless, it is the best available explanation of the origin of species.

The true story of the debate is thus quite different from the one that has become part of the folklore of science. It is assiduously propagated by secularists and all those who want to spread the idea that religion and science are incompatible.

39.   PIERRE DUHEM, 1861–1916

It is still possible to find histories of science that describe the achievements of the ancient Greeks and then pass immediately to the Renaissance, with perhaps are few contemptuous remarks about the absence of anything significant during the Middle Ages. That such views are no longer tenable is largely due to the work of the French physicist Pierre Duhem.

Duhem was born in Paris in 1861 and studied at the Ecole Normale. He soon established his scientific reputation by studies of thermodynamics and is widely known through his derivation of the Gibbs-Duhem equation. He also had a long-standing interest in the history of mechanics, and was invited to write a series of articles on the subject. He followed the story from the Renaissance back to its medieval roots, and became aware of a continuous development through the Middle Ages. He studied the works of Leonardo da Vinci, and found that he obtained many of his ideas from medieval thinkers. Delving into dusty manuscripts in the Sorbonne, he found evidence of intense intellectual activity during the Middle Ages, and a leading part was played by the masters of the Paris schools, particularly John Buridan and Nicholas Oresme.

Making use of earlier work, and taking into account the Catholic doctrine of creation, Buridan criticised Aristotle's ideas about motion and developed his impetus theory. His ideas were widely published and strongly influenced the subsequent development of mechanics.

Duhem told this story in a series of books: *The Evolution of Mechanics* (1903), *The Origins of Statics* (1905), *Studies of Leonardo da Vinci* in three volumes (1906–13) and finally the ten monumental volumes of *The Structure of the World* (1906–59). All this was done in addition to his main activity as a professor of physics.

Duhem's demonstration of the importance of medieval thought, and particularly of the close connection between the rise of science and Catholic theology, was not welcomed by the anti-clerical establishment of the Third Republic, or by the rationalists and secularists who dominated the historiography of science, and they saw to it that his work was virtually ignored. Tragically, Duhem died in 1916 at the age of 55, leaving the last five volumes of *The Structure of the World* in manuscript. The publishers and the secularists were determined to prevent their publication because they knew that it demolished their beliefs about the Middle Ages. There followed a long battle, and it was not until 1954 that Duhem's daughter Hélène and some of his friends finally succeeded in forcing their publication.

Duhem is considered to be the founder of the history of science, and in the years since his death there have been many studies of medieval science by Alastair Crombie, Anneliese Maier, Marshall Clagett, Edward Grant, Ernest Moody and others that have substantially confirmed his work, though naturally correcting it in some details.

Duhem also worked on the philosophy of science and his book on *The Aim and Structure of Physical Theory* is well known. He maintained that the principal task of a scientific theory is to represent in mathematical terms the experimental laws as simply and exactly as possible, while insisting on the need for common sense to provide assurance about the reality of the world.

Throughout his life, Duhem was an exemplary Catholic, showing great fortitude in the face of many setbacks and sorrows. His beloved wife died in childbirth after less than two years of happy married life. He was excluded from Paris by the hatred of the secularist establishment. Although his health was never strong, he wrote forty books and over four hundred articles. He regularly visited the sick and was generous to the poor.

40.   ALBERT EINSTEIN, 1879–1955

Einstein is recognised as the greatest physicist of the twentieth century, and second only to Newton in the history of the subject. In one year, 1905, he made three major discoveries, the special theory of relativity, the theory of the Brownian motion, and the explanation of the photoelectric effect. In subsequent years he made many more fundamental discoveries, notably the general theory of gravitation.

In his autobiography he recorded that when he was four or five years old his father showed him a compass. He was deeply impressed by the behaviour of the needle, and this experience convinced him that "something deeply hidden had to be behind things." This conviction of a hidden reality that we strive, however imperfectly, to understand, remained with him all his life.

Although his parents were Jewish they were irreligious, but nevertheless Einstein was deeply religious as a child. This ended abruptly at the age of twelve when he realised, from the reading of scientific books, that the stories in the Bible could not be true. He became a fanatic freethinker, deeply sceptical of all kinds of authority. This shows how important it is to explain even to young children that the Bible must be interpreted with care and sensitivity; the superficial literal sense is not always the true one, since its purpose is to convey spiritual truths and not scientific information.

At the age of twelve he also had another seminal experience when he read Euclid's geometry. Its lucidity and certainty deeply impressed him. Here at last was a reliable way to truth. From a few evident axioms it is possible to derive by unassailable rational arguments a whole range of geometrical truths.

In his scientific researches he sought the paths that led to the deepest truths about the world. He remarked that he wanted to re-think the thoughts of "The Old One", and to understand why the world had to be made the way it is. When he was told that the measured deflection of starlight by the sun during a solar eclipse agreed with the prediction of his theory of gravitation he was singularly unmoved. When he was asked what he would have felt if the result had not been what he expected, he replied "Then I would have been sorry for the good Lord; the theory is correct anyway."

The world is constructed in a way that is difficult to understand, but not deliberately confusing. As he remarked, "God is subtle, but He is not malicious." When he was asked by a colleague what he meant by that, he replied: "Nature hides her secret because of her essential loftiness, but not by means of ruse."

Once he was accused of being an atheist, and was asked by a friend whether he believed in God. Einstein replied: "I believe in Spinoza's God, who reveals himself in the harmony of all being, not in a God who concerns himself with the fate and actions of men."

On another occasion he affirmed his "faith in the possibility that the regulations valid for the world of existence are rational, that is comprehensible to reason. I cannot conceive of a genuine scientist without that profound faith.... Science without religion is lame, religion without science is blind."

This belief in the rationality of an objective world is strongly related to his scientific creativity. He stressed that this "knowledge, this feeling, is at the centre of true religiousness. In this sense, and in this sense only, I belong to the ranks of devoutly religious men." Thus the belief in the possibility of mathematical physics is almost identical with religion.

He never accepted quantum mechanics as the last word in physics. To Max Born he wrote: "You believe in God playing dice and I in perfect laws in a world of things existing as real objects which I try to grasp in a wildly speculative way."

41.   GEORGES LEMAITRE, 1894–1966

In all the accounts of the Big Bang theory of the evolution of the universe from a minute singularity about fifteen billion years ago it is rare to find any mention of the originator of the theory, the Belgian Catholic priest Georges Lemaître. It was he who proposed the idea in 1931, and subsequently worked it out in detail.

Georges Lemaître was born in Charleroi and entered the engineering school of the University of Louvain in 1911. He served in the Belgian Army throughout the First World War, and afterwards returned to the university to study mathematical and physical sciences, obtaining his doctorate in 1920. He then entered the seminary of Malines and was ordained priest in 1925. Subsequently he spent a year in Cambridge and also visited Harvard and MIT, returning to Louvain where he remained for the rest of his life.

In 1920 he became interested in Einstein's general theory of relativity and worked with Eddington in Cambridge. In the USA he learned about the red shift in the spectra of extra-galactic nebulae, which suggests that the galaxies are all flying apart from each other. In 1927 he published a paper on the dynamical solutions of Einstein's field equations which was the first attempt to connect relativistic cosmology with the observations of the red shift. His aim was to construct a theory that would, from simple initial conditions, describe the evolution of the universe from a highly condensed initial state to its present large-scale structure. In 1931 he published his theory, then described as the Primeval Atom Hypothesis. This primeval atom was unstable, and exploded to produce the electrons, protons and heavier particles that we find today. This work founded the science of physical cosmology, which has been a major area of scientific research ever since.

In 1936 Pope Pius XI founded the Pontifical Academy of Sciences in order to promote scientific research and thereby to maintain a healthy relationship between the Church and the world of science. Lemaître was named as one of its first members and subsequently served as the second President of the Academy.

As he was a Catholic priest, some people suspected that his theory of the Big Bang was suggested by the idea of creation. He was, however, extremely careful to maintain a rigid distinction between the methodology of science and those of philosophy and theology, and was in principle quite opposed to using scientific theories as arguments for the existence of God or His creative activity. He was well aware of the tentative character of scientific theories and opposed their use to support philosophical or theological statements, maintaining that the Primeval Atom Hypothesis should be judged solely as a physical theory.

Lemaître worked on many other problems including the cosmic radiation which he thought might be the remains of the original explosion. Subsequent research, however, has not provided any support for this idea. He also studied the motion of the cosmic rays in the earth's magnetic field, and calculated the dependence of their intensity on the latitude. He studied several mathematical problems, in particular the numerical solution of differential equations.

By his work as an astrophysicist Lemaître furthered the aim of the Pontifical Academy to establish the presence of the Church in our modern scientific culture. Even more importantly, by his emphasis on methodological purity he opposed the facile use of scientific results to support philosophical or theological beliefs, and thus helped to preserve the Church from a wrong interpretation or misuse of the results of science.

42.   FRANK SHERWOOD TAYLOR, 1897–1956

The life of Sherwood Taylor, as he was generally known, is of abiding interest and inspiration. Some fifty years ago he was well known as a writer of chemistry textbooks and also of the history of science. Copies of his *Illustrated History of Science* (1955) may still be found in secondhand bookshops. During the First World War he served in an infantry unit of the Honourable Artillery Company. Volunteering to take the place of an older man, he fought in the battle of Passchendaele in 1917 and was severely wounded; ever after he walked with a pronounced limp. After the war he studied chemistry at Lincoln College, Oxford, and graduated in 1921. He then worked on Greek alchemy and was awarded a doctorate by the University of London. He taught chemistry at various public schools until in 1933 he was appointed Assistant Lecturer in Chemistry at Queen Mary College of the University of London. In 1940 he was appointed to the Curatorship of the Science Museum in Oxford, and in 1950 moved back to London to become Director of the Science Museum in South Kensington. It was at that time that I came to know him personally, and I still recall his great kindness in spending time with a young research student. Those who knew him well speak of his loyalty to his friends, his shyness and hesitancy in discussion, and his dislike of dissension and anxiety to understand the basis of different opinions. The heavy administrative duties in London took their toll on his health, and he died at the early age of 58.

Sherwood Taylor's main academic interest was in alchemy and he wrote several scholarly books on the alchemists. He was one of the founders of the Society for the Study of Alchemy and founded and edited the journal *Ambix*. He was President of the British Society for the History of Science from 1951–53. He wrote many very successful chemistry textbooks and also large popular books on the history of science. His writings were notable for their scholarship and clarity, and his works on alchemy have permanent value.

He was also attracted by mystics such as Henry Vaughan the Silurist and his twin brother Thomas, and also by William Blake. In his book *The Fourfold Vision* (1945) he argued against materialism and for the unity of science and religion. He affirmed that "I know that the scientific description of nature is as jejune as the chemical analysis of the painting of an old master." God "is immanent in all he preserves and sustains as well as a being transcendent, outside and beyond them." The title of the book comes from a poem of Blake: "Now I a fourfold vision see, And a fourfold vision is given to me ... May God us keep, From single vision and Newton's sleep." In it he recalls walking in the garden of St John's College, Oxford, on a clear sunny autumn morning: "The dahlias were still in bloom and the Michaelmas daisies were covered with great butterflies – tortoise-shells, fritilleries and red admirals. Suddenly I saw the whole scene take on a new figure. Every plant assumed a different and intelligible pattern, and individuality with a meaning that was the plant itself, which, by existing in that pattern, was turned towards God and praising him. So with the butterflies; they were not merely lowly organisms, but intensely alive, clad in the livery of God.... The world was a prayer."

He made a special study of Galileo, and wrote a book on *Galileo and the Freedom of Thought* (1938). Not long after he was received into the Catholic Church. If anyone uses the Galileo case as the basis of an attack on the Church, it is important to urge them to study it as fully as possible, remembering its effect on Sherwood Taylor.

43.   ALISTAIR CROMBIE, 1916–1996

Recently there died in Oxford one of the most distinguished Catholic historians of science of the present century. Alistair Crombie was one of the select band of historians of science whose researches revealed the extensive development of science that took place in medieval times. Although the beginnings of science are to be found in ancient Greece, they were not sufficient to ensure its continuing growth. It was only in the Middle Ages that Catholic theological beliefs about the nature of the material world provided the essential basis of science. It was then that modern science really began and developed into a self-sustaining enterprise, culminating in the mature flowering in the sixteenth century. After Crombie's work, it was no longer possible to maintain that there was no scientific work of any significance during the Middle Ages. He destroyed the secularist version of the history of science, which jumps from the ancient Greeks to the Renaissance, with just a few scathing remarks about the intellectual stagnation of the Middle Ages.

Alistair Crombie began his career as a biologist, and subsequently lectured on the history of science at University College in London, and then taught for many years at Oxford. He made many detailed studies of the history of science, and wrote a series of books that are widely valued, in addition to numerous specialised articles. The most familiar is his *From Augustine to Galileo: Medieval and Early Modern Science*, a meticulous survey of the history of medieval science. In this work, he showed that a new system of scientific thought arises not only from new discoveries, but from looking at the known facts in a new way. This happened in the High Middle Ages, when Catholic theology provided a new way of looking at the material world.

Crombie wrote a detailed study of the scientific work of Robert Grosseteste, one of the first Chancellors of the University of Oxford, who made pioneering studies of the method of experimental science and wrote extensively on optics. In 1961 Crombie directed a Symposium on "The Structure of Scientific Change" where many historians, philosophers of science and scientists reviewed the intellectual, social and technical conditions for scientific discovery and technical invention from antiquity to the present time. The papers presented at this symposium and the commentaries on them were published as a volume entitled *Scientific Change*.

Crombie also wrote two books of essays entitled *Science, Optics and Music in Early Modern and Medieval Thought* and *Science, Art and Nature in Medieval and Modern Thought*. In 1994 there was published his *Styles of Scientific Thinking in the European Tradition*, a massive three-volume 2400-page magisterial analysis of the history of scientific method from ancient times up to the nineteenth century. He was a world authority on Galileo and his work, and had nearly completed a definitive account of Galileo's life and scientific discoveries, together with the controversies they generated.

Alistair Crombie's work is of inestimable value not only to professional historians of science, but also to all those interested in the development of science as an integral part of our Christian Faith and culture. His books deserve to be widely studied, particularly in our schools, seminaries and universities, as they show at the highest level of scholarship the intimate links between science and Faith.

It was my privilege to know Alistair personally from the time we were both at University College London about forty years ago until a few days before his death. He was always a welcoming host, both in Trinity

College and at his home on Boars Hill. He wore his vast learning lightly and was sustained to the end by his deep Catholic Faith.

44.   JOHN DESMOND BERNAL, 1901–1971

Bernal is widely known as a crystallographer and writer of books on the relation of science to society. He was the son of an Irish Catholic gentleman farmer and a well-read American lady. He saw the contrast between the wealthy English Protestant landowners and the abject poverty of the Irish Catholic labourers and this turned him into a revolutionary who wanted to drive the English out of Ireland.

He went to Stonyhurst College and became very pious; indeed he organised a Perpetual Adoration Society among his friends that flourished until it was stopped by the Jesuits. He became interested in science and eventually went to Cambridge, where he was converted to Marxism. He was filled with enthusiasm for the Soviet plan to bring in an era of peace and plenty by state planning on scientific lines.

He graduated in 1923 and went to the Royal Institution in London to work with W.H. Bragg on X-ray crystallography. This enables the positions of the atoms in crystals to be determined, which is extremely important for physics and chemistry, and is now finding applications in molecular biophysics. He determined the structure of graphite and invented a new way of analysing X-ray diffraction pictures.

Bernal was a flamboyant character, with a mass of fair hair and crumpled clothes. He was affectionately known as the Sage, because he seemed to know everything. He bubbled incessantly like a fountain of knowledge of everything under the sun. His behaviour was erratic, his desk chaotic, and he was always dashing off to do something else and never finishing anything. He was extremely generous in giving away his ideas, and showed no envy when others brought them to fruition.

In 1927 he applied for a lectureship in X-ray crystallography in Cambridge and it is greatly to the credit of the interviewers that they appointed him because of his obvious brilliance, although one don sniffily remarked that no one with hair like that could be a sound scholar. Subsequently he became Professor of Physics at Birkbeck College in London.

In addition to his scientific work, he wrote many books on science and society, notably *The Social Function of Science, Science and Industry in the Nineteenth Century, The Science of Science* and *World Without War.* He became a member of the Communist party and often travelled to Russia, where he was warmly received and honoured. Sometimes he allowed his uncritical enthusiasm for the Soviet Union to overcome his scientific judgement, as when he associated himself with Lysenko, the notorious fraud who destroyed the science of genetics in the Soviet Union for a generation and was responsible for the death in Siberia of Vavilov, the greatest of the Russian geneticists.

During the war, he urged that more science should be used to support the war effort. Together with Zuckerman he studied the effect of bombing on Birmingham and Hull, and found no loss of morale. They advised against the bombing of German cities, but were defeated by Cherwell. As a result, tens of thousands of RAF airmen and German civilians died needlessly without hindering German production. He helped the Allied landings in Normandy by making detailed plans of the beaches from aerial photographs.

After the war, he rebuilt his research group, and with his collaborators continued to his pre-war work on viruses and also determined the structure of haemoglobin and insulin. His colleagues included Rosalind Franklin, whose discoveries contributed to the determination of the structure of DNA. Instead of concentrating on his scientific research, Bernal wasted much of his time on useless political committees, lecturing and travel.

I met him personally two or three times towards the end of his life, and he always impressed me as a friendly, cheerful man of great integrity.

45.   DOM GEORGE TEMPLE OSB, 1901–1992

George Temple left school at 17 and began work in an insurance office but soon left to become a laboratory technician at Birkbeck College. This was to prove the stepping stone to a degree course and a remarkable career in mathematics at London, Cambridge and Oxford.

His work as a mathematician ranged from relativity and the quantum theory to the abstractions of functional analysis. In 1928, while a research fellow at Imperial College and later at Trinity College,

Cambridge, he worked on the theory of the electron, putting it into a form consistent with Einstein's relativity. At that time he also wrote a book on the quantum theory. Later on he worked on atomic physics, publishing papers on atomic hydrogen and the Zeeman effect. In the early thirties he moved to the Chair of Mathematics at King's College London and began to work on supersonic aerodynamics. He spent the war years at the Royal Aeronautical Establishment at Farnborough, working on practical problems such as wheel wobble and icing in aircraft. After the war his interests moved towards pure mathematics, and he showed how the very abstract theory of distributions due to Schwartz can be expressed in a much simpler but still rigorous way, greatly helping mathematicians primarily interested in practical problems. Much of this work was done at Oxford, where he moved on being appointed to the Sedleian Chair of Natural Philosophy in 1953. After his retirement in 1968 he wrote a history of mathematics from 1870 to 1970, and continued to write mathematical papers until the end of his life.

During his career he received many honours and distinctions. He was elected to the Royal Society in 1943 and received its Sylvester Medal in 1970. For many years he was Chairman of the Aeronautical Research Council, and for this work he received the CBE in 1955. He took a prominent part in the International Union of Theoretical and Applied Mathematics, serving as Treasurer from 1952 to 1960, President from 1960 to 1964 and Vice-President from 1964 to 1968.

He was received into the Catholic Church in 1919, and his Faith remained the inspiration of his life. His departments were happy places to work, and he was always available to give help and encouragement to his students and colleagues. In both London and Oxford he supported the work of the Catholic Chaplaincies. At Oxford he and his wife frequently attended daily Mass at the Chaplaincy and some years later, when he was a monk of Quarr Abbey, he said Mass there himself during his visits to Oxford. It was during a dinner at the Queen's College, held to celebrate his 80th birthday and the publication of his book on the history of mathematics, that he announced to his astonished colleagues his decision to become a Benedictine monk at Quarr Abbey. He was ordained priest in 1983 and faithfully observed the monastic Rule until the end of his life.

46.   MICHAEL POLANYI, 1891–1976*

Michael Polanyi had a remarkable career. He qualified first in medicine and served as a doctor in the Hungarian Army during the First World War. He then took a doctorate in physical chemistry and worked at the Kaiser Wilhelm Institute in Berlin. In 1933 he moved to Manchester to occupy the Chair of Physical Chemistry, where he established a notable school. By 1948 he had became more interested in problems of social philosophy and epistemology, and Manchester University established a personal Chair for him in Social Studies. Finally his interests turned to the philosophy of science, and he wrote extensively on the problems of the justification of scientific research and its relation to human society. His *Gifford Lectures on Personal Knowledge* are well known, and his other works include *Science, Faith and Society, The Contempt of Freedom, The Logic of Liberty, Scientific Thought and Social Reality, The Study of Man* and *The Tacit Dimension*.

As a philosopher of science, Polanyi had two main concerns, to insist that science is concerned with truth about reality, and secondly to uphold the freedom and integrity of scientific research. He tackled these problems in reaction to the prevailing philosophical views and social movements. Scientific thinking in the twenties and for decades afterwards was strongly influenced by the positivism of Ernst Mach and the Vienna Circle. Polanyi regarded positivism as false and dangerous because it tries to eliminate the subjective element from knowledge, which leads to an impersonal objectivity, thus ruling out the interpretive element that enables the knower to attribute meaning and value to the subject matter. This made it difficult for scientists to claim freedom for science in the name of truth, thus playing into the hands of Marxists who wanted science only to serve socially useful ends.

In the thirties and forties there were several Marxist scientists, particularly Bernal, who urged that science be organised to serve the state. Polanyi realised that this would eventually kill science, and was prominent in the Society for the Freedom of Science, and wrote several of its pamphlets. This led him to his studies in the epistemology of science, and his original contributions to our understanding of how we come to know things. He stressed particularly the tacit dimension in learning, that we

---

* Review of *Christian Doctrine in the Light of Michael Polanyi's Theology of Personal Knowledge* by J. Crewdson. E. Mellen, 1994.

know more than we can tell, and also the importance of the whole, which is always more than the sum of the parts.

Miss Crewdson studied theology in Oxford, and had the opportunity to meet Polanyi frequently, as he was by that time retired and living in that city. She has written a comprehensive account of Polanyi's ideas, and shows their value in tackling theological problems. After a summary of Polanyi's main ideas, she considers theological method and shows how it gives a unitary view of reality. The concept of paradigms, originally due to Polanyi, is explored in a theological context. Chapters follow on creation and evolution, incarnation, redemption and the kingdom of God.

Polanyi's thought is profound and fruitful, and the application of his ideas to theology deserves careful attention.

NUCLEAR

47.   THE HYDROGEN BOMB

The first hydrogen bomb was tested on Bikini atoll in the Pacific on 1st March, 1954. In a broadcast soon after, Professor Rotblat described the two-stage mechanism of the bomb: the fusion of heavy hydrogen isotopes provides the main force of the explosion, and the reaction is detonated by a fission bomb. The explosive power of the hydrogen bomb is about a thousand times that of the Hiroshima bomb but, since the fusion reaction produces very little radioactivity, the radioactive contamination is hardly increased at all.

The radioactive debris from the test explosion fell over a wide area, and some of it fell on the Japanese fishing boat *Fukuryu Maru*. The crew saw the explosion and later on noticed a whitish powder that fell on the boat. About three days later they found that those parts of the skin that had touched the powder became dark red and began to swell up like an ordinary burn. After the boat had returned to port, Professor Yasushi Nishiwaki, a professor of radiation biophysics at Osaka City University School of Medicine, read a report of this in the newspaper and was then asked by the Public Health Department of Osaka to examine some of the tuna fish brought back by the *Fukuryu Maru*. He found that they were highly radioactive, and was able to establish the presence of a range of fission products in the dust he found on the boat itself.

Professor Nishiwaki wrote a detailed article on his findings that was published in the *Atomic Scientists' Journal* for November 1954. These were analysed by Professor Rotblat, who found to his surprise that "fission accounts for most of the energy released by the hydrogen bomb." This was contrary to the general belief at the time that a fission bomb simply served as a detonator to initiate the much more powerful hydrogen reaction. Professor Rotblat then realised that the bomb was rather more complicated: there was an additional third stage composed of a shell of uranium 238. This shell serves the double purpose of holding the reacting mass together for a short time longer, thus increasing the explosive power, and far more importantly boosting the power still further by the extra fissions caused in the uranium 238 by the fast neutrons from the hydrogen reaction. Since the energy per fission is about 200 MeV, and those from the three main fusion reactions are 4.0, 3.3 and 17.7 MeV, it is easy to see that most of the explosive power from such a device comes from fission and not from fusion.

This was a startling conclusion, and shows how an academic scientist, by reasoning from published data, can reach conclusions about matters that are considered most secret by the authorities. Professor Rotblat wrote an article on his work that was published in the *Atomic Scientists' Journal* for March 1955. This was of course a sensational disclosure that received wide publicity. The news that the hydrogen bomb was extremely dirty from the radioactive point of view was not popular with the authorities on either side of the Atlantic, and some pressure was exerted to prevent publication. As editor at the time, I do not recall having any hesitation about publishing this article; it seemed to be our duty to make this knowledge generally available.

48.   NUCLEAR FUSION

Nuclear fusion is billed as the final solution to all our energy problems. The fuel is a component of ordinary water, and so the supply is effectively limitless. Furthermore, it does not have the problems of radioactive waste associated with nuclear fission. It sounds too good to be true. What is nuclear fusion and will it ever fulfil its promise?

Nuclei, the tiny but massive centres of all atoms, range in size from that of hydrogen to that of uranium. The most stable nuclei are those of medium mass around iron in the middle of the periodic table. That is why iron is so plentiful. This means that, in principle, we can release energy either by combining two light nuclei or by breaking up heavy ones. The energy of the hydrogen bomb comes from combining hydrogen nuclei, and that of the atomic bomb from splitting uranium nuclei. The fission process can be controlled so that the energy is released slowly in a safe and controlled way, and this is the source of the energy that powers nuclear reactors. The question is whether it is possible to control the energy released when hydrogen nuclei fuse.

The hydrogen nuclei repel each other electrically, so it is necessary to overcome this repulsion to make them fuse. The only way to do this is to raise them to a very high temperature, several hundred million degrees. In the hydrogen bomb this is done by using a fission bomb as a detonator, and this results in a violent explosion. To be useful as a source of power it must be controlled so that the energy is released gradually.

Over the years there has been much research on this problem. Many years ago, when I was a young research student at Imperial College, another research student, Anthony Ware, was working on this problem a few rooms away. He built a glass doughnut-shaped tube called a torus, filled it with hydrogen and wound copper wires around it. He then sent a large current through the wires, and this raised the hydrogen to a very high temperature. He then looked for the emission of neutrons that would show him that the fusion reaction had taken place. At that time this was academic research, and we all discussed it freely. Then the Government realised its immense commercial possibilities and decided that it must be kept secret. The Professor, Sir George Thomson, said that he would have no secret work in his department, and so Anthony and his apparatus were sent to Aldermaston and we heard no more about it. Later on, Dr Ware worked on fusion in Texas.

The problem of igniting a controlled fusion reaction proved to be more difficult that was initially thought and during the following decades many larger torus machines were built in the UK, the USA, Russia and Japan. One of the most successful is the JET (Joint European Torus) project at Culham in Oxfordshire. The scientists there succeeded in maintaining a fusion reaction for about a second, and produced an intense burst of neutrons and two megawatts of power. There are plans to build a much larger machine called ITER (International Thermonuclear Reactor) supported jointly by Europe, the USA, Russia and Japan, but this is now threatened by the collapse of the Russian economy and the financial crises in the Far East.

Even if ITER is built and is successful, it will be many years before a commercial fusion power station can be built. It will use deuterium, a heavier type of hydrogen that is present in ordinary water in the proportion of one to about 5,000, so there will be no shortage of fuel. Although it will not produce the radioactive fission products that constitute the waste from the present nuclear power stations, it will still produce some radioactivity from the interaction of the neutrons produced in the fusion reaction with the surrounding material.

The road to fusion power is still long and hard, but it is a bright hope for the future.

49.   IS NUCLEAR POWER UNACCEPTABLE?

It is now a strongly held politically-correct belief that nuclear power is bad. This belief is so strongly held that meetings arranged by the Government to discuss what to do about global warming do not even discuss nuclear power, even though it is demonstrably the only way to achieve massive reductions in greenhouse gas emissions. If the danger from climate change due to global warming is as serious as the Government believes, there is surely every reason to explore all possible ways to reduce greenhouse gas emissions, and yet this is not done.

This neglect would perhaps be understandable if nuclear power was a minor source of energy that makes no difference to the situation, but in fact nuclear power is now responsible for generating about 20% of the world's electricity, is almost completely non-polluting, is safe and reliable and does not contribute significantly to global warming and is comparable in cost to other major energy sources, particularly when the indirect costs due to the pollution associated with other sources are taken into account.

If those responsible for the decision to ignore nuclear power are questioned, the same arguments are brought out again and again, even though they have been answered in detail many times.

When nuclear power first became available, it was hailed enthusiastically as the power source of the future. What happened to bring about such a striking change in public opinion? The answer is simple: it is the result of a highly successful propaganda campaign that has several roots. Twenty or thirty years ago there was a strong campaign against nuclear weapons and in favour of nuclear disarmament that was supported and partly financed by the Soviet Union. Their long-term strategy was to weaken the West, so that they could eventually conquer it. They could do this first by eliminating nuclear weapons, and then by hindering the development of nuclear power stations, which promised to be increasingly important to the economies of Western countries as the oil supplies dried up.

When the Soviet Union collapsed, the supporters of the campaign for nuclear disarmament found a new cause in the campaign against nuclear power stations. Like all well-planned campaigns, it was based on true statements, so that it was easy to gain the support of well-intentioned persons. To serve their purpose, these true statements had to be exaggerated out of all proportion, and other aspects of the problems ignored, so that they became false. Thus it is true that nuclear power plants have disastrous accidents, so these are continually emphasised. (But the Chernobyl reactor was badly designed and the safety circuits were switched off). It is true that nuclear radiations can kill. (But reactors and radioactive material can be shielded so that none of it gets near us). It is true that nuclear waste is dangerous. (But it can be put in sealed containers and safely buried where it can do no harm). Incessant emphasis on such things, without mentioning the balancing arguments, gradually, over the years, implanted the present conviction that nuclear power is bad.

So strong is the feeling against nuclear power, that it almost impossible to counter it. Thus I was once discussing Sellafield in a newspaper correspondence and sent a letter saying that coal power stations actually emit more radioactivity that nuclear power stations. This was countered by another letter saying that this was obviously absurd. So I sent another letter explaining that coal contains traces of uranium and some of this it emitted in the smoke, and giving the numerical results of a study conduced by the International Atomic Energy Agency that supported my remarks. This letter was not published.

At present, there is no informed, balanced debate on this vital question.

50.   CHERNOBYL AFTER FIVE YEARS

The fifth anniversary of the Chernobyl disaster provides an opportunity for an assessment of the consequences both for the inhabitants of the surrounding area and for the future of nuclear power.

It was, without any doubt, a major disaster. Indeed in a recent Oxford lecture Zhores Medvedev, the Russian dissident and one-time Head of the Institute of Radiological Biology in Obninsk, said that it was one of the main factors leading to the collapse of the Soviet Union. A short time before Chernobyl, Mr Gorbachev's energy policy for the Soviet Union put increasing reliance on nuclear power. After Chernobyl, local anti-nuclear pressure stopped nearly all further construction and thus gravely exacerbated the economic difficulties that already faced him.

Around the time of the fifth anniversary, the media were filled with stories about the consequences of the accident for the people in the surrounding regions, giving substantial figures for the death toll, and for the expected number of cancer cases. It is important to assess the actual evidence, and this can only be done on the basis of detailed measurements of the radioactive contamination. This information is now available from several surveys carried out by international organisations.

The workers in the immediate vicinity of the reactor at the time of the accident received large doses of radiation, and 31 died soon after. In addition, there were 145 people who received large but not fatal doses; they are being carefully monitored and it is likely that some of them will develop cancers over the coming years.

After the initial power surge, the reactor caught fire and large amounts of radioactivity were released. Depending on the prevailing winds, some of this was deposited on the ground in the region surrounding the reactor, and some was carried large distances and was detected in many European countries. To minimise the danger to their health, the authorities evacuated over a hundred thousand people from the region extending about thirty kilometres around the reactor, and they have still not returned.

There are thus two questions to be addressed. Firstly, how seriously is the surrounding region contaminated, and will it ever be safe for the inhabitants to return? Second, what will be the effects of the much smaller doses received throughout Europe and elsewhere?

It is easy to detect the radioactive decay of a single nucleus, so exceedingly minute amounts of radioactivity can be measured. It is therefore already well known that practically everything is radioactive to some extent, including our own bodies. We are continually irradiated by the cosmic radiation from outside the earth, and by the radioactivity in the ground. This constitutes the natural background of radiation, and provides a standard with which to assess the likely effects of any additional radiation due to the nuclear industry, to medical irradiation and to accidents like Chernobyl. Furthermore, the natural background varies very markedly from place to place, depending on the geology of the region. In Cornwall, for example, the natural background is over twice the average for Britain, due to the granite rocks that contain uranium.

Measurements of the radiation levels around Chernobyl show an excess over the natural level due to the accident. Detailed maps have been made and show a very irregular distribution, impossible to summarise concisely. All that can be done is to give a few numbers to indicate the general levels found. All the following numbers are for levels of radiation expressed in terms of the unit microsieverts per hour.

The highest readings were of course near the reactor itself, being 30–50 at 300 metres. Further away, in the town of Pripyat, they were 0.5 to 0.9 and at the edge of the 30 km zone around the reactor, 0.7. In an administration building 18 km from the reactor, 0.2. For comparison, the Swedish scientists who made these measurements in September 1990 found a level of 1.9 on the plane to Moscow. The average British exposure from natural radiation is 0.25, and that in Cornwall 0.85. From such figures it can be concluded that apart from the immediate vicinity of the reactor, the radiation levels are similar to those in Cornwall, or less.

This picture is confirmed by observations of the flora and fauna. Doreen Stoneham from the Oxford Research Laboratory for Archaeology visited the area in 1990 and found deserted gardens flourishing with fruit trees laden with apricots, cherries, apples and greengages, and an abundance of flowers including rosebay, willow herb, wild chicory, thyme, cow parsley and verbascum. Birds were nesting in the chimneys of abandoned houses and in one nest there were two young storks. The only obvious damage was to the older pine trees.

Pripyat was derelict, with creepers growing over walls and pavements. Inside buildings the doses averaged 0.25, but outside they were much higher; 3–8 on the grass, 12 on exposed brick and 110 on another grass verge. She concluded that the contamination of the bricks is a difficult problem, but the biggest obstacle to re-occupation is the deterioration of the buildings themselves after years of neglect.

The health of the million or so people still living in 2,700 settlements in the contaminated area was studied by 200 international experts from 22 countries co-ordinated by the International Atomic Energy Agency and the results have been published in an 800-page technical report. The project was led by the Director of the Hiroshima Radiation Effects Foundation and included members of the World Health Organisation, the International Labour Organisation, the UN Scientific Committee on the Effects of Atomic Radiation and three other independent organisations. It is thus difficult to accept the claims of certain environmental groups that their report was a political whitewash and that they were duped by the Soviet authorities. The report found no health disorders directly attributable to radiation exposure, and in particular no indications of an increased incidence of cancer, apart from childhood thyroid cancer, which is easily curable.

To establish the presence of any adverse health effect, it is necessary to compare the observed incidence with that expected in the absence of the accident. Thus for example it has been reported that there have been 6,000 deaths among the workers engaged on the clean-up operation, but this is just about the number that would have been expected from other causes in the very large number of people involved (some 600,000) over the period in question. There is a tendency to attribute every illness to the effects of Chernobyl, whether or not it is of a type that can be caused by radiation. Every sufferer from leukaemia is officially classified as a "victim of Chernobyl", and is entitled to compensation. Groups of children who have been sent to recuperate in other countries have been found to suffer from malnutrition, but not from the effects of radiation.

This conclusion is supported by the results of Professor Kellerer from Germany, who found that the people in the Chernobyl area thought that the conditions were the result of radiation, and did not understand "that the undoubted deterioration of their health was the result of changed lifestyles and an enormous degree of anxiety, a sort of self-amplifying problem. People believe they are surrounded by problems and they do not drink local milk, rear no poultry and keep children indoors. So quite understandably you have an increased morbidity."

Undoubtedly there has been much suffering due to the evacuation itself, and even more due to the very natural fears of the effects of radiation, not helped by the media. Indeed, the international project commented: "The psychological problems were wholly disproportionate to the biological significance of the radioactive contamination. The consequences of the accident are inextricably linked with the many socio-economic and political developments that were occurring in the USSR. A large proportion of the population have serious concerns. The vast majority of adults examined in both contaminated and control settlements either believed or suspected that they had illness due to radiation."

This was underlined by a report from four Swedish scientists who visited the area in 1990. They were distressed to find widespread evidence of ill-health, but noted that it was not induced by radiation. They believed that "many people are exploiting the biggest consequences of the Chernobyl accident – the radiophobia – to further their own aims." Before the disaster there was chronic malnutrition, and now people are afraid to eat or go outdoors.

Soviet experts are well aware of this, but their reassurances are undermined by local officials with their own political interests. The Swedish scientists interviewed Professor Guskowa, a member of the Soviet Academy of Science, and noted: "When we took our leave of Angelina Guskowa we said goodbye to a very pessimistic woman who all her professional life has been engaged on work at home and abroad to cure people suffering from the effects of radiation, to spread information about these effects and who has endeavoured to estimate the risks of radiation. It was obvious that she was disappointed in how the egotistical interests of politicians and suchlike who, totally without support for such a claim, pose as experts, and have managed to sabotage everything she has worked for."

What of the effects of the radioactive contamination of Europe as a whole? Here again the deposition was extremely patchy, depending on the winds and the rain. Salzburg even received more than Kiev. The additional radiation received by people in Europe was far below the natural background, so it is not easy to estimate the effects on health. The effects of large radiation doses are well known, but almost nothing is known for certain about the effects of very small doses. It could be that the body is able to repair any damage due to very small doses. There is even some evidence that very small doses are beneficial to health. In Cornwall, for example, the incidence of leukaemia is rather less than in the rest of Britain. Nevertheless, in spite of this, it is usual to assume that the effect of radiation is strictly proportional to the dose. This is almost certainly a very pessimistic assumption.

Making the assumption of proportionality, it is easy to obtain figures like the 40,000 deaths worldwide over the next 50 years quoted in the media. This would be statistically undetectable among 500 million people expected to die of cancer in any case in the same period.

Once again the natural background provides a standard for judgement. The extra doses due to Chernobyl are very small compared with other increases we accept without hesitation, such a those on airplane flights, on mountains (due to the cosmic radiation, which becomes more intense with increasing height) and due to the variations from one place to another. There has been discussion about whether more people should be evacuated from the Chernobyl neighbourhood, but none about evacuation from Cornwall, which has a higher natural radiation level.

There were even reports of radiation effects beyond Europe. A much publicised news item reported a strong correlation between mortality rates and the radiation levels from Chernobyl dust in the USA. This looked very convincing, until one reflected that if such minuscule amounts of dust could have such pronounced effects in the USA then the much larger (though still very small) amounts received in Europe would have spectacular effects, which were not present. Examination of the basic data showed that the alleged correlation was spurious. By that time the media had lost interest in the story and had gone on to the next radiation scare.

After Chernobyl several countries, such as Sweden and Switzerland, voted to phase out nuclear power as soon as practicable. But when they looked into the alternatives they realised that they were even less attractive. Coal is seriously polluting, and is contributing to acid rain and to the greenhouse effect. Oil will become more expensive, and it is politically undesirable to rely on it. Hydroelectric power is already used to the practicable limit in most European countries, and the renewables such as wind and solar are not credible as large-scale sources. So the resolutions to phase out nuclear power are being quietly forgotten.

The whole story of Chernobyl is one of tragic and misguided muddle that has brought death to some people and suffering to many hundreds of thousands of others. It is important to examine it carefully, with due regard for the facts, to see what lessons can be drawn for the future.

The nuclear physicists and engineers have developed a new source of energy that has many advantages over the alternatives as regards availability, capacity, safety, cost and effects on the environment. But like most modern technologies, it is complicated and has to be handled with due care. This is not confined to nuclear power; it applies to all industrial processes and modes of transport. The choice is ours, both individually and as members of society. We do not entrust a car, let alone an airliner, to one who is not properly trained, and if we were to do so we would be asking for trouble. In the case of new technologies, it is the duty of governments to lay down and enforce strict rules of operation. Indeed nowadays, when the effects of a major disaster are felt worldwide, it is arguably the duty of the United Nations to do this.

At this point the duty of the scientists and engineers ceases, and that of the politicians begins. It is now clear that the politicians in the Soviet Union failed in their duty. The reactors were built hurriedly for the dual purpose of producing weapons-grade plutonium and providing power for civil use. To achieve this, a design was adopted that would never have been accepted in the West. It was basically unsafe, in the sense that when operating at low power it was thermally unstable; that is, a small extra power increase reinforced the increase instead of producing a cooling that would tend to reduce the power to the desired level. To prevent a dangerous situation developing, strict operating instructions were laid down.

Unfortunately people do not always obey instructions, and on the night of the disaster the reactor was run at low power so that the operators could make a certain experiment. In the interests of safety, the reactor was designed to shut down automatically if it was operated in the unstable region. However the operators realised that this might spoil their experiment, so they switched off the safety devices, and disaster followed. There was no one in the control room who understood the risks that they were taking by trying to make this experiment.

All this could never have happened if the design and construction of reactors had been carried out under the control of an international regulating body.

When the disaster occurred, the scientists and technicians around the reactor, aided by fire-fighters, fought with extreme bravery to control the reactor, and many paid with their lives. The politicians reacted by imposing secrecy until the accident became known internationally and they had to admit that it occurred. The evacuation of the people was probably essential in the circumstances, but not enough was done to give the people accurate information concerning the hazards associated with the doses that they had received.

Local politicians reacted by using the disaster to advance their own political ambitions. The politicians in other countries reacted with panic and voted to phase out nuclear power without a proper study of the implications. The people most affected who lived in the area around the reactor were not given accurate information about radiation hazards, and so they were terrified by the inflated stories abounding in the press and many of them suffered severe psychological problems. They became apathetic and feared to eat readily available food. In the end the dangers to health from this were far larger than the dangers attributable to radiation.

Soon after the accident, a massive clean-up operation was started, and this has continued with international assistance. Extensive measurements have been made of radiation levels to determine when it is safe for the population to return. A major problem remains to heal the deep psychological wounds.

And what of the Chernobyl-type reactors, not only in what was the USSR but also in Eastern Europe? Many, if not most of them are seriously inadequate by Western standards. Should they not be shut down at once? This extreme measure is unnecessary, and would cause widespread hardship and serious disruption of the economy. The Chernobyl disaster occurred as a result not only of design faults but also of a whole series of gross operating errors, including switching off the safety devices. With responsible operating procedures, they can be operated safely. Nevertheless, it remains urgent to modify them to bring them up to international standards, and this is now being done with the help of the International Atomic Energy Agency.

The development of nuclear power has remained in the hands of the politicians, and they have failed to inform the public about its potentialities, and failed to adopt a long-term energy policy. The mass media, for a variety of reasons, launched a wholly dishonest propaganda campaign against nuclear power, and gradually succeeded in convincing the public that it is dangerous and uneconomic.

Ignoring the basic realities causes immense suffering, but in the end reality prevails. Practically ignored by the mass media, a quiet revolution has been taking place in power generation. Already nuclear has displaced coal as the main generator of electricity in Western Europe. France is 80% nuclear, and several other countries are around 50%. Oil is expected to become increasingly difficult to find over the coming decades, not to mention the political uncertainties. Apart from nuclear, coal is the only practicable large-scale alternative, but it is less attractive due to the pollution it causes.

The Chernobyl disaster was certainly a severe set-back to nuclear power, but over the coming years its advantages will steadily become clearer. Chernobyl will remain as a stern reminder that modern technology must be handled in a responsible way if it is to yield its benefits for us all.

51.   CHILDHOOD LEUKAEMIA NEAR SELLAFIELD

It has been known for many years that there are more cases of childhood leukaemia near the nuclear reprocessing plant at Sellafield than would be expected from the average proportion of such cases over the whole country. The number of cases is small, five in all, but is well above the expected number. Naturally this has given rise to great anxiety, and inevitably they have been attributed to nuclear radiations from Sellafield. This has been widely used by anti-nuclear groups in their campaign to close Sellafield, and has had a wide effect due to the special concern associated with children suffering from cancer.

The attribution of the extra cases to nuclear radiations from Sellafield has always been difficult to believe because the minute amounts of radiation that come from Sellafield are far smaller than the natural background radiation to which we are all exposed all the time. Nevertheless, it is known that nuclear radiations do cause cancer, and so the association was readily accepted. Furthermore, if the extra cases are not due to Sellafield, then what is the explanation?

It is most important for those living near nuclear plants and for those operating the plants, to find the answer to this question, and an enormous amount of research has been devoted to the problem.

In 1987 Gardner suggested that the children developed leukaemia as a result of their father's exposure to nuclear radiation, and collected statistics that supported this view. This led to several court cases in which families sought compensation from British Nuclear Fuels, the company operating the plant. However, studies of the children of atomic bomb survivors who received much larger doses of nuclear radiation showed no increased mutation rate. Further studies of a much larger number of children showed no correlation with parental irradiation. Summarising this evidence, Sir Richard Doll and colleagues concluded that the Gardner hypothesis is not proven.

Another possible explanation was suggested by Dr Kinlen, namely that it is due to the mixing of populations. When a large number of people move into a new area, population mixing takes place. This hypothesis can easily be tested, and the results have recently been published in a paper by Dickinson and Parker in the September number of the *British Journal of Cancer*.

In this work, the authors examined the records of 100,000 children born in Cumbria between 1969 and 1989. They found that the more population mixing (that is the proportion of parents in the area born outside Cumbria) the higher the rate of two types of childhood leukaemia. Furthermore, they found that the degree of population mixing in the

Sellafield area was high, and not statistically different from the level expected from the Kinlen hypothesis. Sir Richard Doll has concluded that "the time may have come when Kinlen's hypothesis can be regarded as established." Several other studies, for example in Greece and Hong Kong, have supported this conclusion.

Predictably, these results have been attacked by Green groups, who seem to be more concerned with their campaign against nuclear power than with establishing the facts. Their work has diverted much research effort away from studies of the real causes of childhood leukaemia, and by encouraging families to sue British Nuclear Fuels they caused much unnecessary distress, intensified when inevitably they lost their cases.

This shows again the importance of not jumping to conclusions, especially when they seem to support some political agenda. It is essential, though often hard and laborious, to undertake the research necessary to establish the truth.

52. WISHFUL THINKING ON GLOBAL WARMING

It has recently been admitted by the chief American negotiator at the 1992 Rio Earth Summit that "America, the world's largest polluter, cannot deliver the cuts in greenhouse gases which President Clinton promised by 2010." This provides one more example of the modern tendency to believe that urgent moral problems can be solved by politics or by legislation without paying proper attention to the underlying scientific realities.

The greenhouse gases, mainly carbon dioxide that comes from the burning of coal or oil, are emitted from fossil fuel power stations, by cars and lorries and by many other industrial processes. Emissions can be reduced by moderating the energy demand or by generating the electricity in non-polluting ways, and each of these runs into formidable political difficulties. America is a rapidly-growing technological society that requires electricity for transport, communications and computers, so the demand will inevitably rise in the future. The pollution due to cars and lorries can be reduced by increasing the price of fuel, but to make a significant impact on the problem the price increase would have to be so large as to be politically unacceptable. As a result, greenhouse gas emissions are projected to rise by 30 to 40% above 1990 levels by 2010, whereas at the Kyoto Conference America pledged a 7% reduction.

Is it possible to generate the electricity needed in non-polluting ways? In principle, given the political will, the answer is yes, but not on the promised timescale. The so-called renewable energy sources, such as wind turbines, are ideal non-polluting sources, but they are unfortunately quite unable to produce power on the scale needed. Thus in the UK, wind power produces only 0.16% of our electricity. The only large-scale non-fossil burning power source is the atomic nucleus, and the conversion to nuclear has indeed reduced greenhouse gas emissions in many countries. Thus France (80% nuclear) has halved its emissions since 1970, Japan (32% nuclear) has achieved a reduction of 20%, while the USA (20% nuclear) has achieved only 6%. Thus by replacing its fossil-fuel burning power stations by nuclear ones, America could eventually reduce its greenhouse gas emissions to the promised level. However, this is not possible by 2010 partly because nuclear power stations take a long time to build but mainly because of the strong public opinion against nuclear. The activities of environmental groups have affected public opinion so strongly that discussions of the means to combat global warming frequently make no mention of nuclear power. In an area where it is essential to make careful objective analyses, considering and evaluating all possible methods, it has become a taboo subject. The situation is similar in this country. Our Government has set a target of a 20% reduction, and by 1998 had achieved a reduction of 6%, due to the increase in nuclear output. Greenhouse gas emission is however set to rise steeply in the future as the older nuclear power stations retire. There is another over-riding consideration. At the present rate of consumption world supplies of oil and gas are likely to last only about sixty years, and what will happen then? Our coal resources will last somewhat longer, about two hundred years. If we burn them we increase the likelihood of global warming and also pollute the atmosphere with poisonous gases like sulphur dioxide and the oxides of nitrogen. Furthermore, they are precious resources that will be needed for centuries to come. Do we not have a responsibility towards future generations to use them as frugally as we can, and to develop alternative non-polluting sources before it is too late?

53.　GREENHOUSE GASES AND THE NUCLEAR TABOO

The latest attempt by the Government to meet the reduction of greenhouse gas emission promised at the Kyoto meeting is Mr Prescott's energy tax. The cost to British industry is estimated to be one and three-quarter billion pounds, and will fall mainly on the energy-intensive steel, chemical, cement, glass, clay, paper and foundry industries. This huge extra burden is bitterly opposed by the industries, who know that this will inevitably lead to increased costs for their products, thus reducing their competitive power and probably leading to reduced sales and enforced redundancies. The Government has offered a lower tax to companies signing energy efficiency agreements and also to those who meet agreed reductions in emissions. They also promise a half per cent reduction in employer's National Insurance bills. Nevertheless much of the burden remains, and it is expected that the proposed tax will put many energy-intensive users out of business.

Commenting on this the *Daily Telegraph* on 30th March remarked: "The best joke of all is that the justification of the energy tax is bogus in the first place. The Kyoto targets for carbon dioxide emission could be met by allowing the construction of gas-fired power stations, to replace the coal-fired ones." This option has however been vetoed by the Government, so as not to offend the coal industry.

The truth behind all this can be seen by comparing the carbon dioxide emission from coal and gas power stations. These are 870 for coal and 500 for gas, each in tonnes of carbon dioxide per GWh (gigawatt-hour). Thus there is a reduction by switching to gas, but only by about 40%, but this reduction is offset by the probable leakage of methane, which has a global warming potential over sixty times that of carbon dioxide. These two effects are estimated to be about the same, and if this is so there is NO reduction in greenhouse gas emission to be expected from the switch from coal to gas.

Once again there is no mention whatever of the other possible way to reduce greenhouse gas emissions, namely by switching to nuclear power stations. They do indeed also emit carbon dioxide, at the rate of eight tonnes per GWh, that is less than 1% of the emission from coal power stations. Already the French have halved their carbon dioxide emissions by building nuclear power stations, and other countries with smaller nuclear programmes have achieved less spectacular reductions.

All this shows once more that it is not possible to discuss such subjects seriously without expressing the quantities involved numerically, and also the persistence of the anti-nuclear taboo, which prevents the most effective way to reduce carbon dioxide emissions from even being mentioned.

Another example of this is in a report on a workshop organised by the Scottish Office and the Economic and Social Research Council on "a climate change mitigation strategy for Scotland". At the meeting, every possibility was discussed except nuclear. All the report said about nuclear was that "Scotland has nuclear power but much of this will close in the near future." One would not think from this that 55% of Scotland's electricity is nuclear-generated, and that this will continue for the foreseeable future.

It is hardly possible to believe that people can behave in this way and expect to be taken seriously. It is not a service to society as a whole to ignore the basic facts underlying our energy problems. This is not only a scientific and technological problem; it is an essential moral requirement that we make sure of the facts before reaching decisions.

54.   GREEN ENERGY – FACTS AND FANTASIES

Recently I wrote an article in the *Tablet* on "Green Energy – Hard Choices" This was the latest of a long series of largely fruitless attempts, extending over more than forty years, to shift the nuclear debate from the land of fantasy to a serious consideration of the urgent problems that confront us. It is, I believe, the responsibility of scientists to bring some of the essential facts to the fore, so that the debate can be conducted in a realistic way. I regret that I could not mention everything, which would not have been possible even if I had filled all the pages of the *Tablet*. What is important is to realise that vital decisions have to be made now if we are to survive the energy crisis, and that we have no hope of making sensible decisions without a careful analysis of all the available energy sources according to their capacity, cost, safety, reliability and effects on the environment. The global situation must be studied; it is not sufficient, for example, to say that this or that energy source is dangerous, and that therefore it must not be used. The question is how dangerous is it in comparison with the other possible energy sources. To be realistic, this comparison must be as far as possible expressed numerically, for only then can commensurable quantities be compared. There are other decisions concerning incommensurable qualities such as cost versus environmental effects, that require extensive debate and informed judgement. These analyses must be made by each country in the context of the whole global situation.

At the present time the debate is obscured by a number of fantasies and doubtful beliefs, so perhaps it is useful to mention some of them:

1. *The solution to the energy crisis is increased energy efficiency.* It is certainly very important to increase the efficiency of energy use. Much energy is now wasted. It is not however easy to achieve this. Extra insulation, for example, itself costs energy. To save energy, exhortation is useless. It could be done by increased prices, but this would penalise the poor. Differential tariffs might be the answer. If increased efficiency results in a lower price, this will stimulate demand. However, when all this is said, it is still necessary to produce energy in the first place, and since the demand for energy is increasing, we still need to find new energy sources.

2. *We can get all the energy we need from the benign renewables such as wind and solar.* At present the contribution of the renewables to world energy needs is a few per cent (excluding hydroelectric, which is in a different category and is limited by the available rivers), and it is not easy to increase this without subsidies. The costs will gradually come down, but it is doubtful if they will compete with coal or nuclear. If they do, then it will be time to consider deploying them on a large scale. However, no amount of research can ever make them reliable, and this is a crippling disadvantage. Large scale deployment of wind or solar power has serious environmental disadvantages. Finally, they are by no means benign (see below).

3. *We must only use energy sources that are perfectly safe.* Alas, this is fantasy. All energy sources take their toll in deaths and injuries, due to mining, construction and distribution accidents, oil well fires, dam bursts and nuclear disasters. While these risks can never be eliminated, they can be reduced as far as is reasonably possible. In addition, when making our energy choices, we need to be aware of the risk of various sources. Thus the numbers of deaths per thousand megawatt-years of energy are approximately 40 for coal, 10 for oil, five for wind and solar, one for nuclear and 0.5 for gas. There has been intense debate about these

figures, but they are reasonably reliable and it is likely that the ordering is correct.

4. *All radioactivity is harmful.* We know that large doses are certainly harmful but we simply do not know whether this is true or not for small doses. There is even some evidence that small doses are beneficial. What we do know is that we are continually exposed to nuclear radiations from the radioactive materials in our own bodies, from the earth and from the cosmic radiation. The intensity of these natural radiations varies from one place to another by quite large factors. If we do not worry about this, then it is inconsistent to worry about the far smaller levels of irradiation that come from nuclear power stations or the somewhat larger levels that came from coal power stations.

5. *Nuclear waste is a very serious and intractable problem.* The fission fragments extracted from the spent fuel rods from a nuclear reactor are intensely radioactive and therefore extremely dangerous. So, however, are numerous other chemicals, and they can be contained so that they never come into contact with people. The techniques for doing this for fission fragments are well understood. After a cooling off period, they are fused into an insoluble ceramic, encased in stainless steel and stored in a dry stable geological formation far beneath the earth. The amounts are small compared with the dangerous wastes from the chemical industry.

6. *Every nuclear reactor is teetering on the brink of a Chernobyl disaster.* This is absolutely false. The Chernobyl disaster was the almost inevitable result of an evil political system, and played no small part in its eventual downfall. The design of the reactor, with its inherent instability at low power, would never be accepted in the West. It was built hurriedly to produce plutonium for weapons as well as power, and the workers knew that it would be both useless and personally dangerous to protest at the shoddy construction techniques. The operators were so poorly trained that they embarked on an experiment without understanding what they were doing, and in the course of the experiment switched off the safety circuits. By the time they realised what they had done, it was too late. The result was a disaster. It was a disaster that should not have happened, but to conclude from it that nuclear power should be abandoned is like saying that air travel should be abandoned because an insane pilot flies a plane into a mountain. We now have many thousands of years of experience of operating nuclear power stations

safely and there is no technical reason why this excellent safety record should not continue.

7. *The cases of leukaemia around Sellafield are caused by radioactive emissions.* This was always very difficult to believe since the level of the emissions is far lower than the natural background. It has now been thoroughly studied by unimpeachable medical authorities and shown to be false. Some more details are given in my article in *Blackfriars* for February 1996. It is therefore necessary to look for another explanation for the cases of leukaemia, and it has been plausibly suggested that they are due to viral infections associated with movement of populations.

8. *Nuclear power should be abandoned.* Those who advocate this policy should first say how they propose to meet the world's energy needs in a better way. This means at a comparable cost and with the same or less pollution. Until this is convincingly demonstrated, it is fantasy to suppose that nuclear power stations will be closed down. Nuclear power now provides about 20% of the world's electricity, and in Western Europe the proportion is about 50%. Whether we like it or not, nuclear power is here to stay, and it is very likely to be the principal source of energy, especially in the developed countries, for the foreseeable future.

With these fantasies and misunderstandings out of the way, it is possible to begin to study some of the real problems. The central problem is that vastly increased amounts of energy are required to raise the living standards of a rapidly increasing number of people all over the world. The only sources able to supply the bulk of this energy are coal, oil and nuclear. Oil is fast running out, and in addition it is wasteful to burn a valuable chemical that is the basis of the petrochemical industry. Coal is plentiful, but polluting. Many environmental organisations are doing excellent work in opposing pollution of the atmosphere, and this will inevitably lead to increasing opposition to coal. That leaves nuclear as the only possibility in the long term. This may conceivably change as a result of further research, but until it does we have to make our decisions on the basis of existing knowledge.

Now for the real problems. I suggest a few:

1. *What are our responsibilities to future generations?* We owe it to future generations not to use up materials they will need, or to pollute the earth. The pace of technological change is so great that it is not easy to forecast their needs; for example the development of plastics has greatly reduced the demand for steel. We can foresee that they will need oil, so

it should not be burnt. Uranium is plentiful and widely spread, so that is not much of a problem. Until recently, many industries gave no thought to the pollution they were causing. Now, they are much more conscious of the damage they can cause, and rules are enforced. Industries should try to move to a situation of closed-cycle operation, so that there is no net pollution at all. How can this be achieved in the face of the practical and economic difficulties?

2. *What will happen if nuclear power stations get into the wrong hands?* It is all very well saying that nuclear power is safe in the developed countries, but we can all think of countries with unstable and irresponsible regimes that might fail to take the proper care of their reactors. If a war breaks out, they will be prime targets, and if they are hit, there may be radioactive contamination on the scale of Chernobyl. This is a serious worry, and has led some responsible people to say that we would have been better off without nuclear power. Whether this is so or not, it is too late; the technological clock cannot be turned back. If some way is found to bring the benefits of nuclear power to the Third World countries, it needs to be strictly controlled, perhaps most suitably under the auspices of the United Nations.

3. *How much are we prepared to pay for increased safety?* It is possible to estimate the cost of saving a life by proposed safety features. It is not easy to say what this should be, but at least it should be roughly the same in all circumstances. At present there are glaring anomalies.

4. *How much are we prepared to pay for the preservation and the restoration of the environment, taken in its widest sense?* This includes pollution of the atmosphere, the seas and the earth, and also visual and aural pollution, and the destruction of the countryside. These are extremely important problems that need to be tackled in a realistic and objective way.

5. *What reductions in our lifestyle are we willing to accept?* For example, we cannot go on indefinitely allowing the number of cars to increase; they are a major cause of pollution, destruction of the environment and death. How practicable would it be to increase taxation or to institute tolls to discourage unnecessary motoring?

The above remarks are no more than brief sketches of very complicated questions that must be studied. I certainly do not know the answers, but certainly they deserve to be studied as a matter of urgency.

Wise decisions cannot be made without close attention to the detailed scientific and technological facts.

55.   THE EARTH UNDER THREAT*

This is one of the more authoritative books on the environmental crisis, as is written by Sir Ghillean Prance, the Director of the Royal Botanic Garden, Kew, who is also a convinced Christian. It is short, well-illustrated, easy to read and makes an impressive case for the need to care for the earth. Using several examples from the Amazon rain forest, the royal water lily, the Brazil nut, the calabash, the cacique bird and the three-toed sloth, he shows the intricate interdependence of plant and animal species. There used to be about five million people in Amazonia, but now they are reduced to a bare quarter of a million as their territories are increasingly occupied by settlers, miners and loggers. The natives have an inherited respect for nature, reinforced by tribal taboos, and generally live in a sustainable way, whereas the newcomers are interested only in profit and bring deforestation, loss of precious topsoil, disease and the extinction of species. This is but one example of the devastation of the natural environment that has so dangerously accelerated during the present century. Worldwide, the most serious aspects of the environmental crisis are population growth, global warming, pollution, the loss of biodiversity and the loss of soil.

There are many attempts to tackle these problems, from peasant co-operatives to large international conferences, and some successes have been achieved. Christians have a special responsibility, and many quotations from the Bible show our duty to care for creation, the emphasis being on stewardship rather than dominion. He commends the work of the former Archbishop of Recife and Olinda, who has done so much for the poor. On the other hand, the introduction of Christianity to the Indonesian island of Siberut had a devastating effect. The traditional religions with their taboos against exploiting nature were replaced by a form of Christianity that led to more emphasis on producing surplus for sale, clearing more land, and growing more rice instead of sago. It would have been useful to

---

* Review of *The Earth under Threat* by Sir Ghillian Prance. Wild Goose Publications, Saint Andrew Press, 1996.

probe the theological beliefs of the Christians concerned in these two cases, to see how they are related to the actions taken.

The author considers that the reality of the greenhouse effect and global warming is beyond doubt, and says that whether the temperature increases by 1.5 or 4.5 degrees Centigrade over the next century is "academic". However, as even the lower figure would have serious repercussions for the future, presumably the higher would be even more so. Furthermore, it is disquieting that the range of uncertainty is so large; if we do not know whether it is 1.5 or 4.5, could it conceivably be zero or even less? It might be wiser to say that the effect is rather probable, and this is sufficient to justify action. It is stated that the thermal expansion of the sea water will force the sea level to rise; however this is so only if the expansion of water is greater than that of the earth itself.

It is important to take action to save the earth, and for this to be effective it is essential to evaluate the effects quantitatively. He rightly emphasises the need to switch rapidly to energy sources that do not emit greenhouse gases, and cites solar, wind, hydro, and tidal power, without any evaluation of their capacities, practicabilities and other environmental effects, or indeed of the amounts of greenhouse gases they do emit, for the energy generators themselves have to be made in factories. Most environmental publications categorically reject nuclear power without any discussion, so it is a welcome change to read a cautious acceptance: "…and perhaps even a new generation of safer nuclear reactors in countries which can control the waste adequately." It would be appropriate at this point to give the actual figures for the huge reduction in greenhouse gas emission that is already attributable to existing nuclear power stations as they replace highly polluting coal power stations. Furthermore, a note at the end on the Centre for Alternative Technology says that "we have seen success in the worldwide protests against CFCs, nuclear power, unchecked road building, mass whaling and wasting energy," thus indiscriminately lumping together a range of quite different activities that require careful quantitative analysis before deciding what action would be desirable. Presumably this was not written by Sir Ghillean Prance, and it does no service to his booklet to allow its inclusion.

Action to tackle the environmental crisis can be taken up at two interconnected levels; that by Governments, multinational companies and factory owners on the one hand, and by individuals on the other. The former requires international and national legislation to establish and enforce pollution controls and to curb the other assaults on the land and the sea, the soil, the plants and the animals. The latter is considered in detail by Sir Ghillean, and he gives an excellent list of actions for individuals and for churches. We really must take these questions seriously, and if everyone renewed their lifestyle the total effect would be immense. In addition, it is important to be make one's views known, for companies and governments are now very sensitive to public opinion.

To be useful as well as effective, public actions have to be well informed. Environmental activists rather too frequently rely on emotional rhetoric instead of careful quantitative scientific analysis, and as a result frequently urge policies that would demonstrably do more harm than good. It is a clear Christian duty to respect the earth, and that means respecting the objective truth about nature. Thus any environmental action must be based on a careful assessment of the results of various possible courses of action. Sir Ghillean Prance has provided an excellent introduction to the dangers threatening our earth, and what we can do about it, and it deserves to be widely read. Its usefulness would be enhanced by a more careful quantitative analysis in some sections, and by an index.

56.   GENETIC EFFECTS OF NUCLEAR RADIATIONS

One of the arguments against nuclear power stations that impresses many people is that whatever the truth about the benefits they can bring, there is always the fear of a nuclear accident that could release radioactive material that could cause genetic effects far into the future.

The fear about genetic damage arose as a result of a study of children born to survivors of the atomic bombing of Hiroshima. The Japanese Women's Institute of Hiroshima arranged for midwives to record every defect among babies born of irradiated survivors of the bombing. This was done more than nine months after the bombing, so that any effects could only arise from damage producing inheritable defects.

The report of the midwives was horrific; the numbers of defects was several times larger than had ever been recorded before. However, the President of the Japanese National Association of Women's Institutes insisted that before the report was published a control study should be made of a similar city that had not been atom-bombed. Osaka was chosen, the survey was made, and the results were the same at those found for Hiroshima. The explanation was that the midwives had recorded every possible defect, even those so small that normally they would have been ignored.

These results have been confirmed by many subsequent studies. No evidence of genetic effects attributable to the radiation exposure have been found among the 78,000 children born to survivors of the bombing.

Unfortunately the results of the first study became known before those of the control study, and were widely publicised, especially by anti-nuclear campaigners. The truth has never caught up, and many people still believe in the story of the genetic damage due to nuclear radiation.

It should be added that the absence of detectable effects does not mean that there were none. Nuclear radiations do produce some mutations, but the number is undetectably small even for people like the atom bomb survivors who received huge doses of radiation. These in turn are very small compared with the large number of mutations produced by chemical carcinogens.

This story shows that scientific studies can give very misleading results if not properly carried out, and these are liable to be exploited by people with a political axe to grind. In medical studies, the importance of control studies cannot be overestimated.

Modern scientific advances, especially in the field of medicine, are opening up a wide range of new possibilities and dangers, and the best decisions require not only sound moral principles but also a good knowledge of the basic scientific facts. It is thus always a moral imperative to obtain this information before deciding on the best course of action.

57. ENERGY OPTIONS

There are several matters on which we can all agree. The present waste of energy is nothing short of scandalous, and the problems of energy would not be so severe if we were willing to alter our lifestyles. Maybe we should cut out church heating and curtail pilgrimages by jet. Certainly we should try to use our cars less, but the recent outrage at fuel prices shows how reluctant we are to give up our present mode of travel. Our whole way of life needs to be changed. People should live nearer their work or work at home. Most people however do not respond to exhortation and will change their mode of life only when forced by economic necessity. We should certainly give more thought to saving energy, but it is unrealistic to expect that demand will not continue to rise even in the developed countries. We should also not forget the poorer countries which need more energy even to live, let alone to have anything approaching our standard of living.

This brings us back to the problem of continuing to satisfy the present energy demand, let alone that of increasing production to help the poorer countries. The so-called "renewables", such as wind, tidal, wave, photovoltaic and other solar sources, have some useful small-scale applications, but are totally unable to provide the massive amounts of energy that we need. It is wishful thinking to believe otherwise. Detailed analysis shows that they are costly, inefficient, unreliable, relatively dangerous and harmful to the environment. Hydropower is limited by the number of suitable rivers and there is no practicable way of storing its energy except in rather rare circumstances.

If we decide to keep the dwindling oil supplies for the applications that must have oil, such as many forms of transport and the manufacture of petrochemicals, that leaves coal and nuclear as the only possible sources of large-scale reliable and affordable energy. Before saying that nuclear is "risky and dirty" it is necessary to compare it with coal. Coal mining is indeed risky and dirty. Only today the newspapers report a mine explosion in China involving 241 miners, of whom only 81 escaped, and such tragedies are happening all the time. Miners have to work in risky and dirty conditions, and many of them develop serious lung diseases. All methods of generating power are dangerous and lead to deaths and injuries. Comparing coal and nuclear, studies show that these are about forty times more likely for coal than for nuclear. In addition coal-burning directly pollutes the atmosphere which we all breathe. Thousands of tons of sulphur dioxide and nitrogen oxides are emitted every year from each coal power station, in addition to smaller amount of a whole range of other poisonous chemicals. These not only injure our health, but poison lakes and rivers as well as harming forests. By comparison in normal operation a nuclear power station emits very little into the atmosphere, though it does produce a certain amount of radioactive waste that can be stored where it can do no harm.

All the above statements need to be backed up by detailed numerical analyses, but there is no room for them here. Over the last fifty years I have written several books and numerous articles going into all these questions in detail. In order to make a sensible contribution to the nuclear debate it is essential to know what are the results of comparing all possible energy sources according to their capacity, cost, reliability, safety and effects on the environment, always expressing the results numerically whenever possible. Such studies may be found in my recent book *Nuclear Power, Energy and the Environment* published by the Imperial College Press.

58.   THE TOKAI-MURA BLUNDER

The recent accident at the nuclear plant at Tokai-Mura in Japan came as a severe shock, and will inevitably increase the opposition to nuclear power. It shows once again the fallibility of human beings, and that the price of accepting modern technology is eternal vigilance. It seems that whatever care is taken there is always someone who does not know the rules, or ignores them, with disastrous consequences. This applies not only to nuclear power, but right across the board from travels by road (as the recent coach tragedy in South Africa has reminded us) by water and by air, and also in all manufacturing processes. Another recent example is provided by the destruction of the Mars space probe due to a confusion between metric and imperial units in the design specifications.

The Tokai-Mura accident happened in a reprocessing plant, where the used fuel rods from nuclear reactors are treated to separate the fission fragments from the uranium and thorium. The fission fragments have no further use, and are buried in a safe place, while the uranium and plutonium can be made into new fuel rods. The separation process is a purely chemical operation.

To understand what happened requires a short digression on the physics of the nuclear chain reaction. When a nuclear particle called a neutron enters a uranium nucleus it makes it unstable, so that it soon breaks up into two more or less equal pieces, called fission fragments. These fly apart, releasing much energy. During this process, called fission, two or three neutrons are also emitted. These neutrons can enter nearby uranium nuclei, causing them to fission also, with emission of more neutrons. In this chain reaction the number of fissions rises rapidly, and also the amount of energy released. All this happens very quickly, and it soon blows the material apart so that the reaction stops. If the material is prevented from blowing apart it causes a nuclear explosion as in the atomic bomb.

Natural uranium consists of two types, called isotopes, uranium 235 and uranium 238, the numbers indicating the number of nuclear particles (neutrons and protons) that their nuclei contain. Only uranium 235 undergoes fission, so to make a bomb it is necessary to separate it from the uranium 238.

A chain reaction can only take place if the average number of neutrons from each fission that causes a further fission (called the multiplication factor) is greater than one. It always happens that of the two or three neutrons produced by each fission, some are lost either because they are captured by impurities in the uranium or escape from the sides. A nuclear reactor is made of carefully purified materials and is large enough to reduce the probability of escape to a sufficiently low level. During normal operation the multiplication factor is kept closely to one, so that the reaction, and the heat released, happens in a controlled way.

During the reprocessing of the fuel rods, or indeed in any operation involving uranium, it is essential to ensure that there is never enough fissile material in one place for a chain reaction to occur. This is no problem for normal uranium, but if enriched uranium (with a higher proportion of uranium 235) is being handled the critical amount of uranium is much smaller. At Tokai-Mura the workers were engaged in an operation involving a solution containing 2.4 kilograms of uranium. Instead they used 16 kilograms so there was so much uranium in one place that a chain reaction took place. It seems very likely that the uranium was enriched. When the solution went critical, it must have been rapidly converted into steam. The newspaper reports mention that it took some hours to bring the reaction under control, but this seems unlikely. Since the operation was not being carried out in a sealed building, some of the steam escaped.

It is amazing that a uranium solution could have been treated in such a careless way. The three workmen were apparently unaware of the dangers of what they were doing. The uranium solution, instead of being handled in sealed pipes by remote control, was contained in a steel bucket. They all received a very high doses of radiation, which could well prove fatal. Many other workers received lower doses, and could suffer from radiation sickness. The radioactive steam that escaped would affect a region around the plant, depending on the prevailing winds. Apparently beyond a distance of about a hundred yards the radiation level is now back to the normal natural level, to which we are all exposed without noticeable harm.

Chernobyl was a far worse accident, as it took place in a power reactor which burned for several days, sending a plume of highly radioactive smoke high into the atmosphere, whence it affected a very wide area. By contrast, the effects of the Tokai-Mura accident are relatively localised.

The accident will certainly lead to renewed criticism of nuclear power, but since it did not involve a reactor it has no relevance to their safety. What it does emphasise that all associated processes involving uranium must also be treated with extreme care. All staff in charge of operations must be well trained and made fully aware of the potential dangers. Apparently it was the responsibility of the local council authorities to ensure this, but this duty was neglected.

The benefits of modern technology are so great that we cannot do without them. If however, we are to enjoy those fruits without disasters, continual vigilance is essential. It is not sensible or realistic to criticise technology as such, and still more to call for its abolition, for this would soon cause far more damage and reduction in living standards. Instead, everyone can play their part by insisting on high standards of care. This applies to all of us: gas and electricity and cars can be just as life-threatening as uranium.

59.   THE ENERGY CRISIS

The present scare about the availability of petrol is like the first few heavy drops of an impending storm. Over the next few years the price of oil is almost certain to rise beyond its present level of about $30 per barrel. It has been suggested that it may reach $40 or even $50 within a decade or so. To some extent this depends on the decisions made by the OPEC countries, but as the oil gradually runs out they are rather unlikely to miss the opportunity to increase their already huge profits.

The basic, unavoidable facts are well known. At the present rate of consumption oil is predicted to run out in about sixty years, and long before then it will become increasingly scarce. Intensive efforts are being made to find new oilfields, but with rather little success. About two-thirds of the world oil reserves are in the Middle East.

Oil is a valuable chemical, the basis of the petrochemical industries and it is wasteful to burn it while there are alternative supplies of heat.

Furthermore, there are no alternative sources for some applications such as fuel for aeroengines. Lastly, burning oil pollutes the atmosphere. We thus have many reasons to reduce our dependence on oil.

There are several possibilities. For domestic heating and for power stations we can use coal. There is still plenty of coal: world resources are predicted to last two or three hundred years. However, coal mining is dangerous and unpleasant, and burning coal pollutes the atmosphere and possibly produces global warming. Thus it is not a good solution in either the short term or the long term.

Some of the difficulties seem to be insuperable, such as what to use instead of petrol to drive our cars. It is however now technically possible to drive cars from electricity stored in batteries. These batteries can be recharged overnight simply by plugging them into the mains. Models are already on sale that can reach 60 mph and are very suitable for commuting short distances to work. Such journeys are usually through built up areas, so electric propulsion is very suitable. Longer journeys and higher speeds still need petrol engines. The main difficulty is the cost, but this is likely to come down with more efficient manufacture and the economies of mass production.

If the use of such electric cars becomes widespread, this would reduce pollution and lessen our dependence on oil. It does however require more electricity, and to use oil or coal to generate it raises the same problems once more.

The only practicable source of the needed electricity is nuclear. This is almost non-polluting and has the capacity to provide the electricity we need. At present it is somewhat more costly than the alternatives, but this difference is likely to change as the shortage of oil become more apparent and the oil prices rise.

So why are we not building nuclear power stations as quickly as we can? The reason is largely political. There is a strong public aversion to nuclear power stations, largely due to a long media campaign against them, emphasising the safety aspects and the waste disposal problem.

This is an area where we need a strong government, able to take hard decisions for the sake of future generations. The difficulty is that energy problems have a long timescale, whereas governments think in terms of the next election. They want quick results that will appeal to the voters. So they prefer to stick their heads in the sand, like the ostrich, and hope that the problems will go away.

We know that they will not go away, and the longer we postpone facing up to them, the worse will be the final reckoning.

60. BURNING NUCLEAR WASTES

Most of our household waste material is disposed of by burying or by burning in the municipal incinerator, and if it is burned the heat can sometimes be profitably used. But nuclear waste is different. The highly radioactive fission products in the spent fuel rods are a special hazard and the best we can do is to fuse them into an insoluble glassy substance, put them in stainless steel containers and bury them deep underground. The half-lives of many of the fission products are thousands of years, and there is nothing that we can do to alter them. These long-lived fission products are mainly the actinide nuclei, heavier than uranium.

It is however possible to burn nuclear wastes, and there are already active research programmes in several countries to see how this can best be done. There are two possibilities, and both aim at destroying the long-lived nuclides by nuclear reactions.

The first method is to use what is called an actinide burner reactor. In this burner the actinides are irradiated by an intense beam of neutrons from a fast reactor. Many reactions can take place, including fission, neutron capture and (n, 2n) reactions, and these transmute the long-lived actinides into stable or short-lived nuclei, which can then easily be stored until they decay away. Many of the reactions themselves produce neutrons that can transmute or burn nearby actinides. The burner thus acts as a nuclear reactor, except that it is sub-critical and needs an external beam of neutrons to keep it going.

The other method is to irradiate the unwanted actinides by a beam of high-energy protons. These protons hit the actinide nuclei and break them up, a reaction called spallation. The products of these spallation reactions are also stable or short-lived nuclei.

Before these nuclear incinerators can be built, careful studies have to be made of the reactions that will occur, so that the reactors can be designed to operate safely and efficiently. It is also necessary to estimate how much they will cost.

Some of the actinide-burning reactions that will occur are well known, but many of them are not. It is necessary to determine the cross-sections of these reactions before a feasibility study can begin. It is very expensive and often impossible to measure the reaction cross-sections needed, so research is in progress to see how well they can be calculated. Already there are many reliable theories of high-energy nuclear reactions, and much work is going on to improve them.

Until recently there was a strong research programme on these problems in Britain, both in Government establishments and in universities. However, the abandonment of the fast reactor research programme has severely curtailed this work, and it is very likely that it will soon cease altogether. Once again we see the closing of an area of research where Britain has long been among the world leaders. Nevertheless it will continue in the USA and Japan, and in a few years we may hope to see an efficient and environmentally friendly solution to the problem of the disposal of nuclear wastes.

MODERN PHYSICS

61.   EINSTEIN AND RELATIVITY

When it was first put forward, Einstein's theory of relativity took hold of the public imagination. Einstein, with his wayward hair and absent-minded manner, probing the mysteries of the universe by pure thought, was just what they expected a scientist to be. Journalists waxed lyrical and soon people were saying that Einstein had shown that everything is relative. This is clearly unacceptable to a wide range of believers from Christians to Communists and so the theory was attacked from many directions. It was bitterly criticised both by the Communists in Russia and by the Nazis in Germany. In Boston, an eminent cleric described relativity as "befogged speculations producing universal doubt about God and His Creation" and "cloaking the ghastly apparition of atheism".

The then Archbishop of Canterbury, Randall Davidson, was told by Lord Haldane that "relativity was going to have a great effect on theology, and that it was his duty as head of the English Church to make himself acquainted with it." The Archbishop took this advice seriously, obtained several books on the subject, and tried to read them. He did not have much success in his attempts to understand relativity, and indeed was driven to a state of intellectual desperation. He therefore asked Einstein what effect relativity would have on religion, and was told: "None. Relativity is a purely scientific matter and has nothing to do with religion." So that was that.

The Archbishop comes out of this story rather well. In the first place he actually listened to what he was told, and went to the trouble of getting some books on relativity and trying to understand what it was all about. He made the usual assumption that any highly-educated arts man can in a few hours master any scientific subject, but soon realised his mistake. Then instead of forgetting about the whole matter, he asked a scientist for his advice, and chose a scientist who really knew about the subject. If only his example were followed today, we would be spared the acutely embarrassing spectacle of churchmen and churchwomen moralising on scientific and technical matters without having understood the first thing about them.

In spite of the Archbishop's example, the popularity of the theory of relativity among the general public, reinforced by the image of Einstein as the typical scientist, gave impetus to the idea that physics is relative, and thence that everything is relative. If Einstein had called his work the theory of invariance we would perhaps have been spared this nonsense.

A recent example of the way phrases from relativity can be used in a theological context is contained in a book derived from some television programmes on the effects of our new knowledge on theology. Here we read: "It is rare now to find pastoral counsellors referring people to an absolute morality or an absolute set of principles. Spirituality has come to be about exploring one's own frame of reference in order to discover why you see things as you do. How individuals construct reality is more important than how reality is ... in the context of prayer, rigid notions about the present and the past have to loosen up ... where time is flexible relative to each person, the past can be revisited and healed."

Needless to say, this dangerous subjectivism is connected to Einstein's theory only by the name. The author is simply using ill-digested scientific jargon to bolster dubious theological views. Einstein was concerned in his theory to establish the invariant quantities in systems of particles in motion. Furthermore, while the past can be healed, it is false to say that it can be revisited.

62.   QUANTUM MYTHS

Many of the ideas associated with modern physics, especially those of quantum mechanics, have become widely familiar and have affected the way we think about the world and about ourselves. It is commonplace to come across references to the indeterminate nature of the atomic world and its other mysterious properties. Often these references are relatively harmless, but they are sometimes used to give a spurious authenticity to nonsense, for example in the so-called New Age writings. It is therefore important to see to what extent these ideas are true, and in particular to see whether they are really entailed by the physical observations or if they derive from extraneous philosophical ideas that have nothing to do with physics.

Quantum mechanics is an extremely successful theory, used daily by atomic and nuclear physicists in our attempts to understand the natural world. It enables us to calculate many measurable features of a wide range of physical processes, often to astonishing accuracy. While its success is indisputable, there is continuing controversy about its interpretation. One interpretation is dominant, and so it is widely believed that quantum mechanics has shown that matter is inherently fuzzy and indeterminate (as shown by the Heisenberg uncertainty principle), that the law of causality has been disproved, that electrons are both waves and particles, that events take place only due to the action of an observer (Schrödinger's cat), that objects can influence each other over large distances without anything happening in the intervening space, and finally that "reality has evaporated" (Heisenberg).

There is a clear distinction between a physical theory and its interpretation. The physical theory is simply the mathematical formalism together with the rules connecting the formal symbols with the measurable quantities. In the case of quantum mechanics, Schrödinger's equation enables us to calculate the wavefunction relating to a particular phenomenon, and hence the observable characteristics. That is all the physics.

It is of course natural to ask ourselves what is the meaning of the wavefunction, and a variety of answers have been proposed. These are concerned with the interpretation of the formalism and often they derive from prior philosophical beliefs that have nothing to do with physics.

According to the Copenhagen interpretation, the wavefunction contains all that can ever be known about each individual physical system and that it is meaningless to talk about what cannot be known. The wavefunction exists over all space, and the action of the observer collapses the wavefunction to a particular value. Thus we cannot calculate quantum-mechanically the precise instant of decay of a radioactive nucleus, and so that process must be uncaused. We cannot calculate the direction of motion of an electron after it has passed through a narrow slit, so that must be indeterminate.

Quantum mechanics was developed in the nineteen twenties mainly in German-speaking countries where the prevailing philosophy was the logical positivism associated with the Vienna Circle. According to this philosophy, questions that cannot be answered experimentally are meaningless. It is thus meaningless to ask why a radioactive nucleus decayed at a particular instant, or why the electron went in a particular direction. Other apparently quite reasonable questions, such as which slit was traversed by the electron in the celebrated double slit experiment are similarly dismissed as meaningless.

All this was vigorously opposed by Einstein, who believed that science is the result of our ongoing attempts to understand a real, objective world that exists independently of ourselves. Quantum mechanics is but one step along that world. The wavefunction gives the probability distribution of the behaviour of a large number of similar systems. In the context of this interpretation it is possible to maintain that the material world is a completely determined system in which effects follow causes. The Copenhagen myths then disappear: our inability to measure a phenomenon exactly does not imply that it does not take place exactly. The wavefunction then gives the probability distribution of the determined trajectories of the electrons so that to speak of the wave-particle duality is to make the same mistake as to confuse actuarial statements with those relating to an individual. Since a probability is not a thing it does not collapse. Schrödinger's cat dies at a particular time, whether observed or not. We can calculate the probability that a radioactive atom will decay in a certain time interval, but not the actual time of decay.

Einstein's statistical interpretation leaves open the door to the development of a new theory of microscopic phenomena. Several such theories have been proposed, in particular the pilot wave theory and stochastic electrodynamics. Such theories give more detailed accounts of the working of phenomena in terms of "hidden variables", a possibility denied by the Copenhagen interpretation.

In 1932, von Neumann, a distinguished mathematician, proved mathematically that there can be no hidden variables. In 1952, however, Bohm formulated a hidden variable theory, and in 1966 Bell showed that one of the assumptions made by von Neumann, though very plausible, is in fact false. Thus the possibility of hidden variables remains.

The pilot wave theory was originally proposed by de Broglie in the early days of quantum mechanics and if it had been accepted it is likely that quantum mechanics would have been interpreted as a deterministic theory from the beginning. The theory was however criticised by Pauli and abandoned by de Broglie. Years later, when he saw Bohm's work, de Broglie realised how Pauli's objection could be answered, and so the pilot wave theory remains a viable option.

The Copenhagen interpretation not only generates confusing myths, it impedes the development of physics by closing the doors to future work. Thus Bohr stopped Rutherford from searching for nuclear structure by insisting that his quest was meaningless. Now, long after, the study of nuclear structure is well-established. Physicists should not be told not to ask questions. Recent work on the Bell inequalities has been interpreted as a confirmation of Bohr's views, but this is not supported by a detailed examination of the derivation of the inequalities.

It is sometimes said that Einstein in his later years became out of touch with physics, a stubborn lone figure clinging to outmoded beliefs. There were however many other physicists who held similar views, including Planck, von Laue, Schrödinger, Fermi, Feynman and Dirac (in his later years). They realised that the Copenhagen myths are not entailed by the success of quantum mechanics and that it is possible to hold a saner view of the meaning of that very successful theory.

63.   HEISENBERG AND UNCERTAINTY

The quantum world of atoms and nuclei is often described as fuzzy and uncertain, in sharp contrast to the clearcut deterministic world of classical physics. This is illustrated by Heisenberg's uncertainty principle which says, according to most textbooks, that it is not possible to measure at the same time the position and the momentum (or velocity) of an electron, or indeed of any fundamental particle. The more accurately we measure the position, the less we know about the momentum, and vice-versa. More precisely, the product of the uncertainties in the position and in the momentum is always greater than Planck's constant.

The reason for this is not just that the act of measuring one variable disturbs the measurement of the other. Heisenberg meant something much more radical than this: "It is possible to ask whether there is still concealed behind the statistical universe of perception a 'true' universe in which the law of causality would be valid. But such speculations seems to us to be without value and meaningless, for physics must confine itself to the description of the relationship between perceptions." He went on to say that "since all experiments are subjected to the laws of quantum mechanics and thereby to the uncertainty principle the invalidity of the law of causality is definitely proved by quantum mechanics."

If this were true, it would be an example of a profound philosophical conclusion following from a physical theory, and the conclusion would throw doubt on many arguments that invoke the law of causality. It is however incorrect on several counts. Firstly, our inability to measure position and momentum exactly does not imply that the electron does not have an exact position and momentum. This would only follow if one believed the positivistic dictum that what cannot be measured does not exist. Secondly, the uncertainty principle only applies to measurements on a large number of electrons, not of an individual electron. It is easy to show that the position and the momentum of a single electron can indeed be measured much more accurately than specified by the uncertainty principle.

This is unfamiliar even to most physicists and is contrary to what is found in many textbooks on quantum mechanics. The arguments are given in detail in a book by Karl Popper called *Quantum Theory and the Schism in Physics*. He emphasises that "there can be no question whether, according to the quantum theory, an electron can 'have' a precise position and momentum, *it can*." The detailed physics is also described in an article by Leslie Ballentine on the statistical interpretation of quantum mechanics.

Heisenberg's remarks about causality follow from what is called the Copenhagen interpretation of quantum mechanics that gives rise to a whole range of pseudo-problems. The statistical interpretation, due to Einstein, avoids these problems. It gives a conceptually clear account of the behaviour of electrons and other fundamental particles and leaves open the way to a deeper understanding of the physical world. The essential point is that quantum mechanics is a statistical theory that applies only to large numbers of systems, and the fundamental error, that gives rise to all the confusion, is to suppose that it can be applied to just one system.

This story shows how theories of modern physics can be misinterpreted in the context of a false philosophy, in this case positivism, and used to support very general but false conclusions. These quantum myths are very widespread and appeal to those who like to see the world as full of mysteries.

64.   IS THERE A UNIVERSE?*

Although scientists and philosophers have frequently talked about the universe, few if any have faced the fundamental question whether it can be shown that there is indeed a universe. This is obviously an important question for science but also for theology, since, as Professor Jaki remarks,

---

* Review of *Is there a Universe?* by Stanley L. Jaki. Liverpool University Press, 1993.

"theological discourse about revelation has always lacked firm basis and consistency in the measure in which attention failed to be given to the reality of the universe." Furthermore, "the universe remains also the ground that alone can ensure consistency to scientific as well as philosophical discourse."

In this book, an expansion of the Forwood Lectures given at the University of Liverpool in 1992, Professor Jaki gives a comprehensive survey of the development of the concept of the universe from the philosophers of ancient Greece to the cosmologists of today.

Much of the discussion on the universe lacks a clear definition of the term "universe", and Professor Jaki suggests that it means "the totality of consistently-interacting material things". Each word in this definition is necessary. It is the totality, which means that everything is included, so there can be no other universes. Its constituents are consistently-interacting, which means that it is all governed by the same laws and that every part interacts with at least some other parts, another reason for rejecting discourse about other universes. Finally, its constituents are material things, so that for example they do not include ideas or angels; even human beings are not wholly contained in the universe since only our bodies are material things and we are body-soul unities.

Scientists from the 17th to the 19th centuries frequently used the words *mundus, monde, world* and *Welt*, but did not mean the totality of things. They did not even ask the question whether it is possible to know such a totality. By these words they meant the solar system or stars or the Milky Way. In the 18th century the words *coelum, heaven* and *Himmel* usually meant the stellar world in so far as it is known. Thomas Wright was the first to use the word "universe" as meaning all celestial bodies and he maintained that the universe is finite because it is impossible to realise in actuality an infinite number.

It is difficult to maintain that a uniform Newtonian universe is finite, for then it would collapse under its gravitational field. Lambert tried to avoid this by postulating a rotation that exactly balances the inward attraction, but then how can the whole universe rotate with no outside reference point? However if it is infinite the gravitational potential must also be infinite, and the sky must be infinitely bright. Einstein was the first to put forward a contradiction-free scientific discourse about the totality of things subject to the inverse square law of gravitation. Other scientists in the present century failed to speak clearly about the universe as a whole.

Additional confusion was introduced by the Copenhagen interpretation of quantum mechanics that implies that reality is gained only when the wavefunction is collapsed by an observer, thus suggesting that the very existence of the universe is conditional on the presence of an observer. The steady state theory introduced additional incoherence by postulating the continual creation of hydrogen atoms at an unobservably small rate, without any discussion of the actual process whereby these atoms are created. The result of all this is that books on scientific cosmology provide no proof of the existence of the totality of things.

The philosophers of the last few hundred years, from Ockham and Spinoza to Russell, William James and Bergson, despite much discussion, threw no additional light on the subject. In particular, they failed to analyse the meaning of apparently random events, and "began to talk of chance as if it were more than a cover-up for ignorance."

After an extensive review of the scientific and philosophical attempts to come to grips with the universe, Jaki finally gives his answer to the question of the existence of the universe. The starting point of all reasoning, whether theological or scientific, is the direct recognition of the existence of material objects. We further recognise in each existent thing its relation to other existent things; it is not isolated but is a representative of a class of things that share some features and behaviour characteristics. Things interact with each other in an orderly way, and hence, following Aquinas, "it must be that all things should belong to one world." The unity of all things follows from the rationality of God's creative act. God is supremely rational and the world is one "because all things must be arranged in one order, and to one end."

In this way we can establish the validity of the concept of a universe and establish its existence as an object that may be studied scientifically. This provides the basis for all science and in a different way for theology and philosophy. The story of the development of the concept of the universe is told in detail by Jaki with full references to the primary sources. The arguments are often sketched rather briefly, and so the book provides a strong incentive to go back to the original books and papers on the universe.

65.   CREATION AND THE BIG BANG

The ancients believed that the starry heavens are made of perfect and unchangeable matter. Then scientists invented the telescope and found that our sun is one of many billions of stars forming a vast galaxy that we see as the Milky Way. Further studies showed that our galaxy is but one of billions of galaxies spread through the unimaginable vastness of space. Examination of the light from these galaxies showed that they are flying away from each other with velocities that are proportional to their distances; the further away they are, the faster they are moving. This is just what we would expect if they come from a mighty explosion in the distant past, and calculations showed that this took place about fifteen billion years ago. The universe is not static; it is the scene of violent activity.

Scientists want to know how this explosion happened. Using the results obtained from experiments in nuclear and particle physics, it proved possible to reconstruct in quite fine detail the processes that took place a fraction of a second after the explosion began. The results of these calculations agree with known facts about the abundance of the chemical elements. Furthermore, the radiation formed in the first few instants is still present, and its frequency distribution agrees accurately with the predicted values.

Inevitably, one goes on to ask what happened before the Big Bang, as this explosion was called. Have we found evidence of the creation of the universe by God, or did something happen before the Big Bang? Perhaps there was a previous collapse, one of a series of contractions and explosions going on for ever.

Creation is the formation of the universe out of nothing by the power of God, and science by itself can never prove nor disprove that this happened. It is not possible to observe nothing at one time and something afterwards. It is therefore very unwise to argue, as some Christians have done, that the Big Bang theory shows that there is a Creator.

It is however possible for science to decide whether there was a series of explosions and collapses. The question is whether the universe will continue to expand for ever, or whether the expansion will eventually slow down, stop and become a contraction. What actually happens depends on the total mass of the universe. If this mass is greater than a critical value, gravitational attraction will be strong enough to reverse the present expansion. Present indications are that it is somewhat smaller, but it remains possible that some new types of matter may be discovered that will make the total mass exceed the critical value. There are also arguments from relativistic thermodynamics against an eternal series of expansions and contractions.

When it is studied in detail, the evolution of the universe seems to have taken place in a very improbable way. If the properties of matter and the fundamental constants had been very slightly different it would have been impossible to make carbon, an essential element for life. It looks as if the universe has been designed just to making living beings possible. However, what seems now to have been a series of remarkable accidents may later be shown to have a deeper explanation. Thus the idea that there was a period of very rapid inflation soon after the beginning has already provided natural explanations for what seemed previously to be remarkable coincidences.

These scientific developments can reinforce our feelings of wonder at the richness of the universe and the beneficence of the Creator who made it and keeps it continually in being. The reasons for our beliefs, however, are not to be found in science, but in philosophy and theology, aided by the grace of God.

66.   COSMOS AND CREATOR*

The first sentence of Genesis and the first article of the Creed affirm our belief in the creation of heaven and earth by an eternal, omnipotent God, a God completely distinct from his creation and on whom all creation utterly and continually depends. This is the most fundamental of all Christian dogmas; without it there could have been no Incarnation and no Redemption. "The possibility and rationality of revelation rest on the existence of God, on His having made man in his own image, the image of His own rationality, and on His having placed him in a rationally coherent world which provides evidence of its own and man's createdness."

The centrality of Christ gave the dogma of creation a new vitality because the uniqueness of the Incarnation excluded all cyclic theories of the universe and thus emphasised its own uniqueness. The notion of creation out of nothing was thus embedded more firmly in Christian thought than in either Hellenic or Judaic thought. It was again the dogma of the

* Review of *Cosmos and Creator* by Stanley L. Jaki. Edinburgh: Scottish Academic Press, 1980.

Incarnation that helped Christians to unfold the true meaning of the dogma of creation by vindicating the true nature and dignity of created minds in the cosmos. Subsequently, the dogma of creation went on to play a vital part in the rise of modern science, that is, by providing its essential epistemological foundation.

Acceptance or denial of a personal Creator is the most fundamental choice that a man can make, so it is not surprising that the enemies of Christianity have sought to establish in its place the idea of a self-making man in a self-making universe, an idea developed and propagated by Renan, Nietzsche, Spencer, Comte, Marx, Julian Huxley and Monod, among its more recent spokesmen.

Scientists, especially astronomers and cosmologists, have frequently contributed to the debate, for they command the methods used to explore in precise detail the remote past. Can they, in fact, find scientific evidence of creation itself? There is indeed much evidence that our universe is expanding and that at some remote epoch, about fifteen billion years ago, it was in a much more condensed state. It seems impossible for science to probe beyond this, and Whittaker surmised that "we might without impropriety refer to it as the creation."

This was not the only cosmological theory available at that time. According to Bondi, Hoyle and Gold, the universe is in a steady state, maintained at constant density in spite of its expansion by the continuous creation of hydrogen atoms. They did not, however, ascribe this creation to a Creator. The theory has since been discredited by galaxy counts, and by the discovery of the 3°K background radiation by Penzias and Wilson, referred to by journalists as "the echo of creation". Thus a purely scientific confrontation between rival theories became charged with theological overtones.

The basic impropriety of this connection has been clear for a long time. As Aquinas observed, it is impossible to establish by reason alone the coming-to-be of the universe; this is an event beyond the possibility of scientific investigation. If we know anything about this event, it can only be by revelation. The most that can be established scientifically is that there is some remote epoch beyond which science cannot probe. By definition, no scientific investigations can be made before the beginning, and so creation itself cannot be observed.

More recent work has opened up new perspectives in this debate by showing the astonishing singularity of the universe. Einstein's theory of general relativity established cosmology as the science of the totality of consistently-interacting things. Studies of the initial stages of the expansion of the universe gave very specific ratios for the proportions of the different elementary particles and for the total mass. If these had been slightly different a habitable universe would not have developed, and thus the universe is indeed anthropocentric in a far deeper sense than that discredited by Copernicus. The same background radiation strongly suggests that physical processes at the cosmic level are unidirectional, unique and of finite duration.

It is an extraordinary sign of the coherence of the universe that it is possible "to connect with astonishing skill and exactness its configurations billions of years apart and to infer its large-scale features from the properties of its smallest constituents with breath-taking precision." To this, "the most reasonable attitude is to accept it as something given, and given by a Creator."

The foregoing is only a brief sketch of some sections of this challenging book. No mention has been made of the sections on Gödel's theorem, on extra-terrestrial intelligences and on whether our universe is a trap or a home. Professor Jaki expands and unifies many of the themes of his earlier works. Backed by his massive scholarship, this is an essential guide to one of the central intellectual battles of our times.

67.   THEISM, ATHEISM AND BIG BANG COSMOLOGY*

During the present century, and particularly in the last few decades, it has become possible to study the universe as a whole, and to learn how it may have evolved. Many theories have been proposed, and already some of them have been excluded on scientific grounds, most notably the steady state theory of Hoyle, Bondi and Gold and the various oscillating universe theories. The present evidence supports the Big Bang theory that says that the universe came into existence about fifteen billion years ago. The subsequent evolution has been studied in detail, using established results of nuclear and elementary particle physics, and the theory is well supported by experimental observations and measurements. There are many highly speculative elements in the theory, especially concerning the initial phases, but it remains the framework within which current research is conducted.

---

* Review of *Theism, Atheism and Big Bang Cosmology* by William Lane Craig and Quentin Smith. Oxford University Press, 1993.

This theory inevitably stimulates theological questions. Is the Big Bang the actual moment of creation, and if so does it provide an argument for the existence of God? The philosophers Craig and Smith hold sharply differing views, and they present arguments for theism and for atheism in alternate chapters, many of them taken from highly technical papers already published in philosophical journals.

Craig begins with an exposition of the Kalam cosmological argument: (1) Everything that begins to exist has a cause of its existence. (2) The universe began to exist. (3) Therefore the universe has a cause for its existence.

The minor premise is supported by arguments showing that an actual infinity of past time is impossible. Craig discusses in detail the concept of infinity in modern mathematics, but rightly says that this has nothing to do with actual infinities. The Hawking-Penrose singularity theorems show that even for imperfectly homogeneous universes, Einstein's general relativity implies a beginning in time since the past-directed space-time paths end on the singularity. This excludes speculation about what happened before the Big Bang. However, scientific theories, even if well-supported, are in principle revisable, and so the main argument for the minor premise is philosophical.

Smith criticises these arguments but is nevertheless inclined to accept the conclusion. He concentrates his attack on the major premise, citing several recent theories that postulate a spontaneous beginning for the universe. Thus Tryon in 1973 proposed that the universe is the result of a vacuum fluctuation, but this simply moves the problem back as it requires a background space to fluctuate. Vilenkin's theory suggests that the universe appeared as the result of quantum tunnelling from a vacuum. This is unacceptable since, as Aquinas knew, any change requires an enduring existing subject, and this is lacking in creation. It should further be mentioned that these theories are highly speculative with no supporting evidence.

Smith goes on to maintain that it is not necessary to postulate a cause for the universe since Heisenberg's uncertainty principle has shown that there can be uncaused events. However, as Craig points out, unpredictability does not imply acausality. Furthermore, the argument shows a complete misunderstanding of Heisenberg's uncertainty principle, since like all quantum-mechanical statements it refers to the average behaviour of an ensemble of similarly-prepared particles, not to an individual system. Smith thus fails to substantiate his belief that "the fact of the matter is that the most reasonable belief is that we came from nothing, by nothing and for nothing." He is not depressed by this; on the contrary he declares that "we should acknowledge our foundation in nothingness and feel awe at the marvellous fact that we have a chance to participate briefly in this incredible sunburst that interrupts without reason the reign of non-being."

Craig points out that Smith's argument "even if successful, in no way proves that the universe began to exist without a cause, but only that its beginning to exist was unpredictable." Theists agree about this unpredictability, since creation is a freely-willed act of God. Our failure to predict the emergence of the universe "in no way implies that anything and everything can actually come into existence uncaused." He adds that "our conviction of the truth of the causal principle is not based on an inductive survey of existents in spacetime, but rather upon the metaphysical intuition that something cannot come out of nothing." Thus "if the universe did originate from nothing, then that fact does point to a supernatural cause of its origin."

In the second part of the book Smith argues that the Big Bang is incompatible with theism. The Big Bang singularity is such that all the laws of physics break down; it is a "sudden flash of lawlessness that allowed something to come out of nothing". It is thus inherently chaotic and unpredictable and therefore there is no guarantee that it will evolve so as to produce animate life. Yet theists hold that God created the universe specifically for this purpose. According to Big Bang cosmology this is impossible, and therefore theism is false.

This argument may be countered in several ways. Firstly unpredictable by us does not imply unforeseeable by God. Secondly, the theory of the singularity is still very speculative and may be superseded by a different theory. Finally, even granting the chaotic nature of the Big Bang, it remains possible for God to keep the subsequent evolution on the right track by appropriate interventions. Theism does not require a deist God who sets the initial conditions and takes no further interest in the subsequent evolution.

The last two chapters are devoted to analyses of Hawking's theories. Craig shows that "contrary to popular impression, God plays for Hawking an important role as a sort of Leibnizian Sufficient Reason for the universe." However, "Hawking's critique of God's assuming the office of temporally first cause as demonstrated by the Kalam cosmological argument is rife with unexamined and unjustified philosophical asssumptions." Smith, however, finds Hawking's theory physically intelligible, inconsistent with theism and having a superior explanatory value.

These are just a few of the arguments to be found in this stimulating book. The discussions take full account of recent scientific developments in cosmology and quantum gravity, and are articulated with great philosophical sophistication. They have raised the discussion to a higher though somewhat less accessible plane than is to be found in numerous popular accounts of modern cosmology.

68.   GOD AND THE COSMOLOGISTS*

Cosmology, the study of the evolution of the universe, continues to be of great popular interest, reflecting an instinctive realisation that the latest scientific results bear on the most fundamental questions. Many books, often by distinguished scientists, are published on the subject, but their authors often lack the theological and philosophical knowledge to do it justice. It is therefore a pleasure to find a book on cosmology by a physicist who is also a Catholic theologian. Professor Jaki is already well known for his many masterly books on theology and science, including several on the history of astronomy.

In eight chapters he surveys the advances of the last few decades and analyses their theological and philosophical implications, with particular reference to the cosmological argument. He begins by showing that it is only relatively recently that the whole universe, considered as the totality of consistently-interacting things, has become the object of scientific investigation. Einstein's general theory of relativity treats the universe as a whole, and optical and radio telescopes are now able to probe the furthest galaxies. The development of the universe from the initial singularity about fifteen billion years ago can now be described in quantitative detail using the results of nuclear and particle physics.

The universe displays an astonishing specificity. Thus in the early universe, if the ratio of the number of nucleons to that of protons, electrons and neutrinos had been slightly larger or slightly smaller than it is, there

* Review of *God and the Cosmologists* by Stanley L. Jaki. Edinburgh: Scottish Academic Press, 1989. Second Edition, Real View Books, 1998.

would have been no nuclei heavier than hydrogen and so no carbon and no possibility of life. Again, if the force between two protons had been a few per cent stronger, nearly all the matter in the universe would have burned to helium before the galaxy started to expand. There is much similar evidence, all pointing to the conclusion that our universe has evolved along a very narrow path, just the path that made mankind possible. This demands an explanation beyond science.

Scientists wishing to banish the spectre of a Creator supported the steady-state theory of the universe and, when this was disproved experimentally, that of an oscillating universe. Great efforts were made to find the missing mass that would ensure that the current expansion would ultimately turn into a contraction, but it was not realised that even if the missing mass were found the laws of thermodynamics demand that the subsequent oscillations would decrease in amplitude, resulting again in a finite and transitory universe.

There are two basic possibilities: either the universe is dependent on something external to it or its existence is necessary. Scientists who wish to exclude the idea of God thus try to develop an all-encompassing theory that appears to make the universe self-explanatory. However, Gödel showed that in any non-trivial axiomatic system there are always some propositions whose truth cannot be proved within that system. Thus, however successful a cosmological theory may be, we can never prove that it is necessarily true, and thus the contingency of the universe can never be disproved by science.

The development of quantum mechanics in the 1920s provided a means of calculating atomic and nuclear processes with astonishing accuracy, but Jaki opposes its most popular interpretation, stemming from Bohr and his Copenhagen school, which has weakened our grasp of the objective reality of the universe. Heisenberg failed to distinguish between the objective existence of exact quantities and the inability to measure them exactly and declared that "objective reality has evaporated." Sliding still further into subjectivism, he declared that "observations not only disturb what has to be measured, they produce it." In the same vein, Bohr likewise abolished the reality of the universe by saying that "it is wrong to think that the task of physics is to find out how nature is. Physics concerns what we can say about nature." No wonder Einstein and some other prominent physicists deplored the dangerous game the Copenhagen people were playing with reality. With his instinctive realism, he pointedly asked whether the moon still existed when he was not looking at it.

To provide an explanation for evolution in the absence of God, chance is now invoked as if it were itself a causative agent, although it is no more than a word indicating ignorance of the actual causes. If we are able to speak of chance at all, it should be with reference to the apparent unlikelihood of the whole evolutionary process that has led to life on earth and to the emergence of man and of modern science.

The question why modern science arose only in medieval Europe, and not in any of the great civilisations of antiquity, has been studied in detail by Professor Jaki, who argues that it was the Christian beliefs in the contingency and rationality of the world and its creation by God that broke the straitjacket of Aristotelian physics. The essential contribution of Christian theology to the beginning of modern science has been massively documented by the French physicist Pierre Duhem. All this was most uncongenial to the secularist establishment, which saw nothing of value in the Middle Ages, and so it did all in its power to prevent the publication of Duhem's work. It is also uncongenial to Protestant writers who like to place the beginning of modern science in the Renaissance, and not in the Catholic Middle Ages, which are always painted as black as possible.

Jaki seeks to show that Christian beliefs made science possible, and in this way led us to our most specific knowledge of the universe as a whole. This knowledge, unless we are blinded by spurious philosophies, powerfully reinforces the recognition of the necessity of a Creator.

These lectures certainly require close attention if they are to yield their full meaning. The effort is well repaid, for they constitute a detailed and scholarly reply to the over-publicised and ill-informed popular books that harness science to a secular view of the universe.

69.   FINE TUNING THE UNIVERSE

At the basis of physics there are several fundamental constants such as the velocity of light, the gravitational constant, the charge on the electron and Planck's constant. They determine the scale and structure of things and the strength of forces that hold them together. Many studies in recent years have shown that the whole evolution of the universe from the Big Bang to the present is critically dependent on the values of these constants. If they had been very slightly different we would not be here at all.

For example, soon after the Big Bang there was only hydrogen and helium. The astrophysicist Hoyle pointed out that in order to build up carbon, which is the basis of life, the structures of the nuclei of beryllium, carbon and oxygen had to satisfy extremely stringent conditions, and this depends critically on the strength of the nuclear forces.

What can we deduce from this? Hoyle was so impressed by what seemed to him to be extraordinary coincidences that his agnosticism was temporarily shaken. Does it not provide strong evidence that the universe was designed specially for us?

This argument for the existence of a Creator received a setback when it was suggested that an infinite number of universes with different sets of fundamental constants have bubbled randomly out of nothing, so that sooner or later there would appear a universe that has just the values needed to makes our own existence possible. Implicit in this argument is the assumption that these constants can conceivably have a continuous range of values. But for all we know, they may be fixed by considerations about which we know nothing. Indeed, one of the most fundamental questions in all physics is whether it is possible to calculate their magnitudes from some very general theory. Several attempts have indeed been made, but with little success.

There are other objections to this argument. The idea of universes bubbling randomly out of nothing is philosophically objectionable. Basically, there is no such thing as chance; the word simply signifies that we do not know the cause. Furthermore, nothing can come from nothing. To a theist the idea of a God making a series of trial and error attempts to make a habitable universe is incompatible with His almighty power.

In addition, there is a fundamental objection that has been insufficiently noticed. The objection is simply that there is a very limited number of fundamental constants, but also several conditions that combinations of them must satisfy if life is to evolve. The argument is valid only if the number of constants is greater than or equal to the number of conditions. If it is less, then it is impossible to adjust the constants to satisfy the conditions. To my knowledge there is no proof that this is not so.

One may well ask why people look for arguments for the existence of God based on modern astrophysics. The five ways of St Thomas Aquinas remain essentially valid though they may need restating in the light of

144

subsequent knowledge, as indeed St Thomas himself would have done. Certainly our knowledge of the universe is vastly greater than that of the medievals, and this can increase our sense of wonder and with it our belief in the need for a Designer.

Einstein has remarked that "the most incomprehensible thing about the universe is that it is comprehensible." Perhaps this is not so remarkable after all, because God created the universe and ordered it in measure, number and weight (Wisdom 11:21) and stretched His measuring line across it (Job 38:5). God is rational and his universe shares his rationality. He made it as a home for us.

70.   DOWNHILL ALL THE WAY

Scientists are very familiar with the second law of thermodynamics that says that disorder always tends naturally to increase, and that to keep things ordered needs constant effort. Housewives, particularly those with small children, are also familiar with this, and it applies also to the religious life.

More technically, the second law says that entropy, a property of physical systems that can be defined mathematically, always increases. More colloquially, the second law says that you cannot break even. For completeness, the first law says that you cannot win, and the third law that you cannot quit the game. It is a depressing fact of life.

The same principle is also operative in the biological realm. Anyone who looks after a garden knows full well that left to itself it soon becomes a wilderness. Weeds proliferate and strangle the flowers. It requires continual effort to keep the weeds in check and the garden tidy.

The same applies to the spiritual life. We so easily slip into a routine, attending Mass and saying our prayers without properly attending to what is really happening. We let slide our opportunities to help others, and ignore altogether our obligation to bring the world to Christ. We have a natural tendency to evil that is called original sin and this downward slide can only be counteracted by continual effort. Quite often it is only some unexpected event or tragedy that shakes us out of our routine and forces us to renew our lives.

This tendency of everything to slide downhill defines the direction of time. If we are shown a film of a glass being shattered or of milk being stirred into coffee, we have no difficulty in saying whether the film is being run backwards or forwards. Our cup of coffee gradually cools until it reaches the same temperature as its surroundings. In the end the whole universe will run down until it is all at the same temperature, and nothing further can happen; this is called the heat death of the universe.

From the point of view of fundamental physics there is a serious difficulty with all this. The equations of motion of Newton and Schrödinger are time-reversible, so that they are unchanged by reversing the direction of time. How, then, can we account for the second law of thermodynamics?

This problem was tackled by physicists in the nineteenth century, particularly by Maxwell and Boltzmann, who developed the theory called statistical mechanics that provided the answer. Every fundamental process is indeed time-reversible, so that in a system of interacting particles all possible outcomes are equally probable. The ordered outcomes are however very few, while the number of disordered outcomes is enormous. It is thus not absolutely certain that disorder will always increase; the contrary is just extremely improbable. This remote possibility provides no comfort at all. Even for small simple systems, the probability of entropy decreasing significantly is so small that it is very unlikely to happen during the lifetime of the universe. You are never going to see your cup of coffee spontaneously get hotter, although this is not absolutely impossible.

There is a final twist to this story. Quite recently it has been found that the interactions of some short-lived fundamental particles called kaons do not have time-reversal symmetry, so that the direction of time can be given an absolute basis in physics. This will not, however, affect the general tendency for everything to slide downhill into chaos, unless we make strenuous efforts to counteract it.

PHILOSOPHY OF SCIENCE

71. STYLES OF SCIENTIFIC THINKING*

Science as we know it today has a long history stretching back to the Greeks and the Babylonians. It is essentially the results of our continuing attempts to understand the natural world, and as such it is conditioned by our culture, by our beliefs concerning what is important and what is not, about the nature and purpose of knowledge, and about the structure of argument and the criteria of proof. These factors vary from one culture to another, and together they determine the style of scientific thinking.

It was very difficult to get started, and fatally easy to become trapped in a blind alley. Early civilisations amassed much natural lore, and extensive astronomical observations were made, notably by the Babylonians. But the chief credit for initiating the scientific enterprise belongs to the ancient Greeks.

The whole scientific enterprise, as Alistair Crombie points out in his magisterial treatise, depends first of all on the underlying vision of reality, and then on the arguments used to support and verify that vision. The Greek philosophers provided both the vision and the argument. The first idea was that the vast complexity of the world can be understood in terms of simple elements; once we know these elements we can see how everything else follows from them, giving an integrated knowledge of the whole. The rules of rational inference were codified into the science of logic, and an outstanding example of the power of rational argument was provided by Euclid.

This immediately raises serious difficulties: how are we to find out about these elements, and how are we to connect them to the world of nature? The early Ionian philosophers simply postulated the elements: all is water (Thales) or all is composed of earth, air, fire and water (Anaximander).

It was Plato who realised that mathematics can be used to understand the world. He postulated a world of pure forms that are imperfectly realised in matter. The forms are mathematical, and thus we

---

* Review of *Styles of Scientific Thinking in the European Tradition: The History of Argument and Explanation especially in the Mathematical and Biomedical Sciences and Arts* by Alistair Crombie. London: Duckworth, 1996.

can understand the harmonies in nature, for example the simple numerical ratios between the musical harmonics.

A more extensive scheme, embracing all fields of knowledge, was elaborated by Aristotle. He saw the whole of nature as governed by laws; everything that happens has a cause, everything that moves has a mover. This implies that there must be a first cause or Prime Mover. All that we see is thus deducible from fundamental principles, and he tried to obtain these principles by rational argument. Thus for example he was impressed by the difference between the celestial world of the stars and the planets, where there seems to be no change, and the terrestrial world where things grow and decay. Everything is perfect in the celestial world, and so the planets must move in circular orbits, since the circle is the most perfect curve. The celestial world is eternal and incorruptible; the terrestrial world is changeable and corruptible.

Reacting against the materialism of the atomists Leucippus and Democritus, who maintained that all is atoms and the void, Aristotle tried to save purpose, and hence human freedom, by postulating that all material beings seek their natural place. Thus fire rises upwards whereas stones fall downwards towards the earth. In this way he was able to give a quantitative account of many natural phenomena.

This method of studying nature is too general and superficial; it fails to tell us exactly why things behave as they do, and so does not enable us to test whether the postulated principles are true. The intuitive approach is too simple and optimistic; the world is not open to our imagination and the truths of science are not so easily won. Aristotle indeed realised that the natural world must be carefully examined, and was himself an acute observer of biological phenomena. He failed however to observe inanimate phenomena with the same care; thus he attributed the Milky Way to mist from the marshes without noticing that it is unchangeable, and carelessly maintained that when things fall, their velocities are proportional to their masses. He thus failed to understand the importance of precise measurement, which was well understood by other Greeks such as Archimedes.

Aristotle's philosophy had a great and enduring influence on subsequent thought because it provided an all-embracing framework for the analysis of human activities, rationally ordered and persuasively articulated. Most people were justly impressed by the profundity of his philosophy and were not so sensitive to the defects of his physics. The result of this was that further advances were inhibited and science was trapped in a blind alley for over a thousand years.

A new style of scientific thinking came from an unexpected quarter, from the Revelation given by God to the Hebrews. The God of Abraham, Isaac and Jacob was very different from the Prime Mover of Aristotle. God freely chooses whether to create or not, and what form His creation takes. The world is not a necessary world, like that of Plato and Aristotle, so it cannot be apprehended by pure thought. We have to examine it in detail to find out how God in fact made it. The world is not eternal; it was created in time. It reflects God's rationality and obeys His laws, and so there is no reason to distinguish between the celestial and the terrestrial bodies. God ordered everything in measure, number and weight, and so a precise quantitative study of the world is essential if that order is to be found.

The first attempts to confront Greek and Hebrew thought were made by the Jewish philosopher Philo Judaeus of Alexandria in the first century BC, and this was continued by Lactantius in the 3rd century AD, Augustine in the 5th and by John Philoponus in the 6th. The Incarnation of Christ strongly reinforced the Hebrew vision of the world as it enhanced the dignity of matter and destroyed the cyclic view of time that was such a debilitating feature of all ancient cultures.

The doctrine of creation was of particular importance for the development of modern science because of its influence on the philosophical discussions in the Middle Ages. The works of the Greek philosophers became known in the universities of Western Europe during the High Middle Ages, and it was soon realised that their sophistication and comprehensiveness provided the means to articulate the Christian Faith in a more profound way. Intense discussions took place, particularly in Paris, and eventually the bishop, Etienne Tempier, found it necessary to condemn 217 propositions as contrary to the Faith. Among these were many concerning creation, in particular several restricting God's power. The effect of this was to channel thought in fruitful directions, leading eventually to the rise of modern science.

The medieval philosophers greatly admired Aristotle but nevertheless did not hesitate to differ from him when he contradicted Christian doctrines such as the creation of the world in time. Thinking about creation John Buridan realised that when God created the world He gave an impetus to every material body that enabled it to continue in motion. He thus contradicted Aristotle's dictum that everything that moves is continually acted upon by a mover, and adumbrated the conservation of momentum, eventually to become Newton's First Law of Motion.

Experimental science was also developed in medieval times, following the logical methods of Aristotle that were designed to analyse the relations of cause and effect. In the hands of Robert Grosseteste and William of Ockham these were developed into systematic procedures by which hypotheses were tested by examining their consequences both logically and by comparison with experiment. Grosseteste based his physics on a theory of light, seen as the most fundamental form of energy, and thus paved the way to the mathematisation of nature. He saw light as an instrument used by God to produce all creation, from the celestial spheres to the human body, and thus it is the cause of all subsequent changes. He studied the reflection and refraction of light, and other optical phenomena such as the colours and geometry of the rainbow. This work was continued by Witelow, Pecham and Theodoric of Freiburg. Thomas Bradwardine was the first to try to quantify motion by connecting variables by algebraic functions. Further studies were made by William Heytesbury, Richard Swineshead and John of Dumbleton.

The extent and sophistication of medieval science, now very well known through the work of Duhem, Crombie, Mayer, Grant and many others, is sufficient to refute the view, favoured by secularists and Protestants, that the Middle Ages were periods of intellectual stagnation and ignorance, and that science flowered only in the Renaissance when the domination of medieval theology was ended.

The medieval belief in the order of the universe encouraged accurate measurements that can be used to test general principles. Thus Kepler toiled for years to find the orbit of the planet Mars, believing it to be circular. He failed to fit the accurate data of Tycho Brahe, and eventually realised that the orbit is elliptical, thus contradicting Aristotle's *a priori* reasoning.

Galileo adopted the medieval idea of studying concomitant variables and relating them algebraically. He saw that the way ahead was not through general speculations but careful and detailed analysis of specific well-defined problems. Thus he measured the time taken by balls to roll down inclined planes,and found that the distanced travelled is proportional to the square of the time taken. He made the first telescope and immediately observed the satellites of Jupiter, which tended to support the Copernican heliocentric system. He also observed sunspots, which were seen as a blemish on the perfect celestial realm.

Galileo's discoveries offended the Aristotelian establishment, and soon he was in trouble for his support of Copernicus. They asked how he could explain the passage in Scripture where it is said that the sun stood still, implying that normally it is in motion. He was told by his friend Cardinal Bellarmine that there would be no difficulty if he simply said that heliocentrism was a mere calculational device, with no pretence to represent reality. He admitted that if definite proofs of the earth's motion were found, then the question of the interpretation should be looked at again. This did not satisfy Galileo, who said that the Scriptures were given to teach us the way to salvation, not to provide us with information about the world that we could find out about by reason and experiment. At that time, however, a definitive proof of heliocentrism was not known; this came years later with the work of Foucault and Bradley. Nevertheless, Galileo vigorously propagated his views with more skill than tact, with well-known consequences.

Subsequently, Newton postulated his laws of motion, and showed that they account for the elliptical orbits of the planets as well as the observations of Galileo, thus unifying celestial and terrestrial dynamics. The demolition of Aristotelian physics was complete and modern science was established in a state of unending growth.

From the sixteenth century onwards there was great interest in the historical development of mankind, the goal being the identification of the causes of change. The method consisted in trying to find a common origin of a class of phenomena. It was first applied to the comparative study of languages in order to establish how they are related to each other and how they have diversified from a single postulated source. Matthew Hale saw an analogy between the development of languages from a common origin and the development of living things, and Leibniz established the comparative method as a systematic discipline.

Francis Bacon believed that the goal of history is the discovery of causes and saw the history of thought as central to any account of mankind. He saw himself as the inaugurator of a new scientific epoch, and tried to specify the scientific method in a way that would guarantee progress. He hoped that from the increased understanding of nature would come the improvement of man's estate. He believed that he had succeeded in firmly linking the empirical and the rational. His role was more that of a philosopher of history than of science, and he believed that the true purpose of knowledge is not for pleasure or for profit but for the benefit and the use of life.

It was increasingly realised that science is a co-operative endeavour, and groups of scientists banded together to form national academies that provided opportunities for discussion and facilitated exchange of news about the latest discoveries.

In the eighteenth century there was increasing emphasis on the history of science and of mankind in general, with emphasis on explanation through a search for origins. This was partly and in different ways the legacy of Descartes and Locke. The philosophical histories often relied more on imaginative reconstruction than on established facts, which were in short supply for the earliest times. The need for more facts stimulated extensive anthropological studies of primitive societies and languages in order to obtain some insight into the development of our own. Herder insisted on the need for careful observations of man in all his aspects, and offered "a philosophical history of humanity within a Leibnizian history of nature. He saw in the whole history of nature and mankind a providential teleology designed to generate in succession first the general structure of the universe and then, within the special conditions of the solar system, the Earth and on it the sequence leading from inanimate materials up through plants and animals to man. Each stage was designed to prepare for the next, all leading to humanity, to man with his rational and moral capacities as the final product."

There was intense debate between philosophers like Maupertuis, Buffon and Herder who insisted on an unbridgeable gap between man and the nearest animal and those like La Mettrie and Rousseau who argued for a real affinity between them. La Mettrie tried to prove that man and animals are both machines, with different organisations, whereas Rousseau saw apes not as machines, but as men in a natural state. This discussion stimulated further interest in the evolution of languages, and attempts were made to educate apes, without much success.

Complementing these studies of the history of man were parallel studies of the history of nature, from the origin of the world until the present time. Until the seventeenth century most philosophers were more concerned with nature as it is now, rather than with how it came to be. At first the discussion centred on the complex interaction between the revelation in Genesis and the ancient Greek cosmogonies, particularly that in the Timaeus. Twelfth century philosophers like Thierry of Chartres looked for natural causes as well as divine reasons, and much later Descartes tried to reduce the laws of nature to those of matter in motion. He suggested that the existing universe could have been generated by the operation of purely physical laws on the primal chaos created by God. This was highly speculative, but the subsequent detailed studies of geology and biology provided a vast body of empirical evidence to be explained by evolutionary theory. Fossils looking like fish skeletons were found high in the mountains, suggesting a long process of geological change. Early estimates of the time taken for such changes expanded the time scale of the earth's history far beyond the 6000 years apparently implied by Scripture.

The study of fossils suggested that species have changed in the past, and this idea was supported by the success of breeders of new plants and animals. Extensive studies were made of the structure of plants and the anatomy of animals, and the many similarities were classified by Linnaeus. Buffon saw that this could imply a common origin, and conjectured how species developed from simple molecules. Lamarck improved Linnaeus' classification of the animal kingdom, basing it on fundamental anatomy, and proposed that species are gradually transformed by the inheritance of acquired characteristics. Cuvier on the other hand stressed the effects of the surroundings and attributed the similarity of living organisms to a common response to functional needs.

These descriptions of the development of species left open the question of the effective agent. Paley saw the intricate organisations of plant and animal forms as evidence of design, and considered it incredible that it could all have come about by chance. Lyall used such theological ideas to guide his research into the ecology and geology of creation, following unchanging laws. Inspired by Malthus, Darwin and Wallace found in natural selection, acting on chance variations, the agent of evolution. Their achievement was to develop a new vision and to provide massive evidence in its support. They were able to explain, in broad outline, how species could change and adapt themselves to new environments. Darwin saw in this a nobler conception of design than that afforded by a series of individual creations, but did not see the process of change as leading in any particular direction; it is simply a series of progressive adaptations made in order to survive. The idea of evolution had been around for a long time, but Darwin and Wallace showed that effective originality required not only ideas but also the detailed painstaking work necessary to reveal their consequences.

These brief reflections on the effects of styles of scientific thinking on the development of science give scant indication of the vast scope and massive scholarship of Alistair Crombie's three-volume work. There are extensive references to the literature, and the notes, bibliography and index alone run to nearly a thousand pages.

In all, he identifies six styles of scientific thinking, each of them identified by the object of enquiry, the questions posed and the answers accepted. These styles are firstly postulation, exemplified by the Greek realisation that mathematics could account for some of the simple regularities of nature. Then there is the experimental argument, a way to search for principles in more complicated phenomena, as exemplified by the medieval logic of experiment and also the rational artists of the Renaissance. This led to hypothetical modelling comprising the imitation of nature by analogical models, giving insight into the working of nature. The studies in the 17th and 18th centuries of the taxonomy of living things, the logic of ordering by agreement and difference, provides a fourth style. Studies of the random processes underlying change required the development of probabilistic and statistical analysis allowing probability to be quantified. Finally there is historical derivation, whereby the diversity of existing things, from languages to living organisms, are traced to a common origin. This style is found throughout history, from the ancient Greeks to more recent times, when it is applied to the history of the human mind and to the cosmological, geological and biological history of nature, culminating in the theory of organic evolution by natural selection.

It is of particular interest to see how at each stage theological ideas have inspired the growth of science, and how the resulting scientific discoveries have in turn influenced theology. Any serious study of these interactions will be greatly indebted to Alistair Crombie for this culmination of his life's work, which puts us all once again immeasurably in his debt.

72. THE RELATION BETWEEN RELIGION AND SCIENCE

There are at least three ways of thinking about the relation between religion and science. The first considers them as two separate entities that have somehow to be related and reconciled. This is done by comparing their subject matters, their methods of attaining truth, and the status of their conclusions. This enables us to list their similarities and their differences and to see whether or not there can be disagreements, or whether they are so separate that they never even come into contact.

The second way, that is now increasingly popular, is to see science as a way to God. It is even maintained that science provides a surer way to God than traditional religions. Religion is thus a fruit, an end-product of scientific research. This is of course flattering to scientists and enables them to write books with great popular appeal. The nature of scientific knowledge, and the provisional character of scientific theories, makes this a very dubious enterprise.

The third way, that I believe to be the correct one, is to see religion as providing the fundamental beliefs about the world that make science possible. Thus Catholic theology tells us that the natural world is good, orderly, rational, contingent and open to the human mind, and these beliefs are essential for science. This enables us to understand why it was that science as we know it now did not develop into a self-sustaining enterprise in any of the great civilisations of antiquity. Science achieved its first viable birth in Western Europe during the High Middle Ages, when for the first time there was a society dominated by Christian beliefs, and the social structure that allowed the free discussion of novel ideas. If we think of science as a tree, religion is to be found among the roots, not among the fruits.

The relation between religion and science is not between abstract entities, but among men and women with different degrees of knowledge, preconceptions and abilities. The participants are theologians, philosophers, scientists, academics, students and people in general. The fruitfulness of the dialogue depends on the degree of mutual understanding, shared presuppositions and readiness to learn among the participants.

Some scientists are keenly aware of the limitations of science and its relations to the rest of knowledge. Others believe that eventually science will solve all problems that are worth solving, and that religion is a harmful distraction that must be stamped out. It is difficult to dialogue with such people.

Some theologians value science for the knowledge it brings and the new possibilities for life that it makes available. Others see it as a threat to religion, an invader that must be repulsed and confined to its methodological domain. All too often this attitude has hindered a fruitful dialogue.

At present we are blessed with a Pope who really values science and has expressed his appreciation of the work of scientists in many addresses and encyclicals, specially in the recent *Fides et Ratio*. He provides an inspiration that is not always followed.

One of the most fruitful forms of religion-science dialogue is that within a person who is both a scientist and a believer. To achieve personal integration,a believing scientist must study the questions at the religion-science interface, to do this effectively requires the guidance of those who have achieved such an integration, especially priest-scientists.

An important task is to ensure that the true relation between religion and science is conveyed to those who are neither theologians nor scientists, and to counter the views of atheists and secularists that at present fill the mass media.

73. THE SCIENTIFIC ATTITUDE

Many of the misunderstandings that arise between science and religion or, more accurately, between scientists and religious people, stem from unfamiliarity with the ways scientists think, how we approach problems, how we test our conclusions and how we present our results. Scientists are engaged in a continuing search for the truth about the natural world. To do this we rely on observations, measurements and experiments, often stimulated and guided by hypotheses and theories. We observe some phenomenon, we make a conjecture about what is going on, we make a mathematical model of the process, we calculate what will happen in certain circumstances and we make an experiment to see if this does indeed happen. If it does, our conjecture is strengthened and we try to think up new ways to test it. If it does not happen as predicted, then we have to modify our model. This process goes on and on until we achieve a good understanding of the phenomenon.

Scientists are always looking at each other's results, criticising them and trying to find ways to test each other's ideas more severely. We repeat each other's experiments and calculations to see if we get the same results.

Nothing is taken on trust. If mistakes are made, they are corrected sooner or later. This is a great strength of science.

Scientists are very well aware how easy it is to make mistakes, or take for granted some idea just because it has always been believed. Examples of this are legion. It was always believed that parity is conserved, namely that nature does not distinguish between left and right hands. More precisely, that two experiments, one a mirror image of the other, will give the same results. Eventually this was tested and found to be false. Again, it was believed that velocities add arithmetically until Einstein showed this to be false.

Sometimes we think that we know how things are going to behave, but it turns out that we are wrong. Thus at one time there was a strong argument against the wave theory of light: it could not be true because it predicted the appearance of a bright spot in the light on the other side of an small illuminated sphere, which seems absurd. However, the experiment was done and the spot was there and so the wave theory was triumphantly vindicated. There are many other examples. Few people would predict the behaviour of a gyroscope or a tip-top and yet the apparently surprising behaviour all follows from classical dynamics.

Such experiences teach scientists to take nothing on trust, to question everything. Naturally this sometimes makes them rather uncomfortable people to have around. It is tiresome to have one's ideas challenged and tested and yet ultimately this is the only way to reach the truth. Ultimately the truth is the only object of the scientist's endeavour, and that obviously should be welcomed. Who in their senses wants to go on believing things that are not true?

Scientists are therefore baffled when they come across people who will not listen to what they are saying, who contradict them without being able to give any reasons, and who go on to prevent their ideas being published. Scientists have a high regard for honesty and a willingness to admit mistakes. We do not care who says something; we want to know what are the arguments, what is the evidence, for any statement.

It is of course true that scientists do not always live up to these high ideals. Often we say things that are unconnected with our scientific work; there is no harm in this unless we use the mantle of science to give credence to statements that have nothing to do with science itself. Some scientists do this and thereby give science a bad name.

74.   ABUSING SCIENCE*

Over the last few years creationists have been very successful in propagating their views, particularly in the USA, where several states have passed legislation requiring that in schools equal time be given to creationism and to the theory of evolution. This has naturally aroused fierce controversy. Scientists who try to argue with creationists soon find that they have a battery of plausible reasons for their views at their fingertips, so that it requires extensive knowledge, considerable debating skills and a dogged persistence to make any headway. Few scientists have the time for this sort of activity, preferring to get on with their own work. It is, however, vital that the battle be fought and won, so a debt of gratitude is due to those like Philip Kitcher who have studied the creationist case in detail and exposed the fallacies of their arguments.

The first and most basic question is whether creationism is genuine science, and to answer this we need clear criteria to distinguish science from pseudo-science. It is one of the few merits of the creationist debate that it forces us to face this question. To answer it adequately requires considerable familiarity with the philosophy of science. A favourite tactic of the creationists is to define science so as to exclude the theory of evolution. It is sufficient to point out that according to their criteria quantum theory fails as well, so that their concept of science is mistaken. The essential marks of genuine science are that it exposes detailed relationships between diverse phenomena, answers a whole range of problems with relatively few interconnected concepts and opens the way to continuing fruitful research.

Judged by these criteria, creationism is scientifically worthless, with no positive achievements whatsoever, while "evolutionary theory received overwhelming support from a diverse body of evidence. It explains the characteristics of organisms, the relationships among groups of organisms, the distribution of plants and animals and the features of the fossil record. 'Scientific' creationism does none of these things. It is an indefinite doctrine that makes up for its paucity of problem-solving success by hurling misleading objections at its intended rival" (p. 176). To establish their case that species were individually created a few thousand years ago, creationists do violence not only to biology, but also to geology and to physics. In the name of tolerance, they try to force science teachers to abuse

* Review of *Abusing Science: The Case Against Creationism* by Philip Kitcher. Open University Press, 1983.

thermodynamics, misread the fossil record and distort the methods of radioactive dating.

Why do they do this, and receive massive support from devout Christians? It is because they believe that the Bible is the literal word of God, and that, in the words of one of their spokesmen, the whole Bible is "the only sure basis for education in religion, in history and in science". Lacking belief in a teaching church having authority to interpret the Bible, and with little appreciation of the subtleties of biblical interpretation, they have no alternative but to read the Bible literally. To deny that Genesis is literally true is for them "out of the question for any real believer in the Bible". Yet, as Kitcher points out, it is possible to hold that Genesis is the inspired word of God, teaching us vital truths about the creation of the world and the relationship of man to nature, expressed in the language of its first hearers.

The creationists' insistence on the special creation of each species leads to a bizarre and pathetically inadequate concept of God. If every species were designed and created individually, it is impossible to understand, for example, the panda's thumb or the orchid's structure, which receive easy and natural evolutionary explanations. This may be done within the conception of a God who created the whole universe billions of years ago, endowing it with properties that led eventually to the formation of the solar system, the development of the rich variety of living things, and finally of man himself.

Creationists reject this unified view, spread confusion among the faithful and invite the derision of scientists. It is indeed true that evolutionary theory has frequently been used by agnostic scientists intent on the destruction of religion, but this is no discredit to its scientific content. It is a disastrous blunder to try to defend religion from such attacks by attempting to undermine science itself.

Philip Kitcher's book will be found most useful by those wishing to straighten out this tangle. As far as can be judged by a physicist the scientific critique is very well done. He is impressively familiar with the detailed biological evidence necessary to tackle each aspect of the creationists' arguments. The theological sections are less well done, although he mentions the more important points. The theological case against creationism is even more devastating than the scientific one, and this could have been brought out more clearly. It is also unfortunate that he makes great play with the legendary encounter between Wilberforce and

Huxley that has become for many the symbol of the defeat of religion by science. As J.R. Lucas has shown (*Historical Journal*, 22.313.1979), the truth is much more complicated, and far less discreditable to Wilberforce than is generally believed.

75.   REVOLUTIONS AND PARADIGMS

There are periods in the history of science when everything seems to go smoothly. There is a well-established theory that seems to account for most of what is known, and so research consists in applying it with increasing accuracy and to a range of new phenomena. This may go on for decades or even centuries as the theory is confirmed to ever higher accuracy. Sooner or later, however, difficulties may appear. A new observation or measurement may not be in accord with the prediction of the theory. The discrepancy may be very small and there is a strong temptation to ignore it or to explain it away. Perhaps it does indeed turn out to be due to some experimental effect that was overlooked, but in other cases the anomaly may refuse to go away. Perhaps several such anomalies appear over the years, and then it is apparent that something is wrong with the theory. This is a time of crisis for science.

The crisis may be prolonged, and reduce scientists to despair. But then someone has a bright idea and develops it into a new theory that explains all the apparently anomalous results and also the successes of the old theory. The scientists can breathe again, and carry on their research along the new lines.

There are several examples of this in the history of science. The most notable being the scientific revolution of the seventeenth century and the development of the new physics in the early decades of the present century.

The seventeenth century saw the replacement of Aristotelian physics by the classical physics of Newton. The Aristotelian view of the universe was that of unaided common sense: a stationary earth with the sun, the stars and the planets revolving around it. It formed the background of the medieval theological synthesis. Gradually, however, it was found to be defective. Many observations could be more easily understood if the earth goes round the sun, just like the other planets. The astronomers were the first to be convinced. Then Newton proposed his three laws of motion and his theory of gravitation and these enabled the motions of the moon and the planets to be calculated to very high accuracy.

For centuries Newtonian dynamics went from strength to strength, and then some small anomalies were found. The motion of the planet Mercury could not be completely understood, and there were serious problems about electromagnetic waves. Eventually these were solved by Einstein's theory of relativity. An even more profound revolution occurred with the development of quantum mechanics.

Thomas Kuhn wrote a book called *The Structure of Scientific Revolutions*. He distinguished between normal science when research goes on using an accepted theory, or paradigm, and the times of crisis when there is a switch to a new and incommensurable paradigm. He likened it to a gestalt switch, as occurs when we see two different interpretations of a picture. It was then argued that this shows that science is subjective and contains no reliable truths. Other theories, such as astrology or creationism, are equally valid.

A more careful analysis shows that there is a strong continuity underlying every scientific revolution. Einstein's theory, for example, gives the same results as Newton's in the limit of small velocities. Without this continuity it would not even be possible to describe the change. The new theory gives a truer picture of the world but the old theory remains true in its more limited area of validity.

These ideas have also been applied to theology, and the Second Vatican Council has been given as an example. It did indeed give us a new way of looking at the world, and an encouragement to action, but the fundamental truths of the Faith remain the same through all the changes.

76.   THE INTERPRETATION OF SIGNS

We are always interpreting signs. We stop at the red traffic lights, we do not park on double yellow lines, and we know the signs for the permitted speed. There is a conventional one-to-one correspondence between the sign and the meaning. It is the same with the letters of the alphabet, and the numbers. Words are also signs, but they are far richer in meaning. Seldom is there a simple one-to-one correspondence between word and meaning, and this, incidentally, is what makes translation so difficult. Many words such as love, sin and soul have acquired over the years a rich variety of meanings that cannot easily be described. In the sciences words like mass and energy, space and time have a variety of meanings acquired over the centuries. To understand what is meant when we see them requires an extensive knowledge of the context, the times and the writer.

The same applies at a deeper level to the natural phenomena studied by the scientist. An observation of some event, a measurement, some tracks in a cloud chamber will mean nothing to a non-scientist. To the scientist, they are full of meaning. Years of study enables the scientist to see the hidden connections and to put them all together to make a coherent picture. This may take weeks or months, and then suddenly it all falls into place. It is difficult, if not impossible, to explain the grounds for this certainty to the non-scientist. There is no simple series of logical steps that leads from the observation or measurement to the conclusion. If one has some other reason to resist the conclusion it is easy make a case that the scientist has difficulty in answering. This probably accounts for many historical misunderstandings such as the Galileo affair.

Another example is provided by X-ray pictures of our bodies. To us they are vague outlines in black and white, but to the trained radiologist they give a wealth of information about incipient diseases that enable remedial action to be taken.

The human mind is thus able to absorb a range of subtle indications and integrate them to give the whole picture. This can only be done by one who is in full command of all the data and is looking for the reality behind the appearances. It is faith seeking understanding.

It is the same at a deeper level when we consider the truths of our Faith. If pressed, most of us would find it difficult to give a precise logical account of our beliefs. It is less a matter of logical deduction and more a matter of our Faith making sense of our lives. Once again, it all fits together. Newman studied it in detail and called it the illative sense.

An example is provided by miracles. These extraordinary cures still happen, and it is always possible to say that here we have an example of a strange process for which we do not yet have a scientific explanation, and leave it at that. There is no logical way to go from the bare facts to the spiritual interpretation. We cannot be forced to believe by the evidence alone. But if we can interpret the signs and integrate the spiritual and the material, then we can recognise a miracle. It is possible for individuals to be wrong, as scientists are sometimes wrong, and so we need the Church to make a final decision after exhaustive examination of all the evidence.

In a similar way we can look at the evolution of the universe from the Big Bang onwards and ask ourselves what happened before then. Science alone says nothing, but it is a pointer that can be interpreted. Similarly we can look at the vast intricate profusion of organic life and ask ourselves whether it could have come about by accident. We can say that we just don't know, or we can see it as sign of something greater.

77. THE RAVAGES OF SUBJECTIVISM AND POLITICAL CORRECTNESS

Scientists sometimes appear to be arrogant; we frequently give the impression that we know what is true and what is not true, and this is sometimes seen to be contrary to the modern view that everyone has the right to his or her own opinions, and that all decisions must be made by popular vote. Some years ago a certain state decreed that in future for general convenience the constant *pi* shall have the value 3; mathematics, however, is not subject to lawyer's decisions. There is only one correct answer to a mathematical problem; it is not decided by popular vote. There is sometimes a useful discussion about the best method to obtain that answer, but no one in his senses doubts that there is a correct answer.

The situation in physics is somewhat more complicated because of the difficulties of measurement and the possibility of different interpretations, but here again there is no doubt among practising scientists that what we are doing is trying to find the truth about an objectively existing world that is independent of ourselves. When eventually, after much toil, light dawns and some phenomenon is (at least partly) understood, then some truth has been attained. It is useless to legislate otherwise, as even the Marx-Leninists discovered. At one time they believed that Einstein's relativity was contrary to their doctrines, and so it was prohibited. But the scientists knew that if they designed their nuclear accelerators ignoring relativity, then on the great day when they were switched on, nothing would happen. Eventually the ideologists realised this, and let the physicists get on with their work in the way it had to be done. Natural laws are objective truths and cannot be flouted. If you ignore the law of gravitation then you are liable to get hurt. It is just the same with moral laws. We may dislike them, but they cannot be changed, not even by the Pope, and if we ignore them we also get hurt.

The belief in the objectivity of truth is becoming weaker. Children in schools are sometimes encouraged to discuss things before they have acquired the most elementary factual knowledge essential for any discussion. Issues of great public importance are decided by the criteria of political correctness, not by what is true. I was once astonished to have my views on nuclear power brushed aside as a consequence of my (presumed) support for the prevailing capitalist-technological society. Whether my views were true or not was not even considered. Indeed in some circles reason itself is derided, and of course it is not possible to have a reasoned discussion with people who despise reason.

It is thus very appropriate and necessary that the Pope in his encyclical letter *Fides et Ratio* emphasises the importance of reason and shows that it is closely linked with Faith. Philosophers are reminded that "the desire for truth is part of human nature itself." It is their vocation to seek the meaning of life, "one of the noblest of human tasks". The urgency of the task of recalling philosophers to their vocation is evident when one sees the ravages of subjectivism and political correctness in contemporary universities as described, for example, by Allan Bloom in his book *The Closing of the American Mind*. Michael Dummett, in a recent article in the *Oxford Magazine*, remarked that the view "that there is no absolute truth, is shared, almost as a routine dogma of professional methodology, by most practitioners of several disciplines: of anthropology, of certain other social sciences, of linguistics and of literary criticism and theory, as well as of history. It is a philosophical view, but it does not occur to practitioners of these subjects to discuss it with their philosophical colleagues." Those philosophers who still believe in their true vocation have much to do. Scientists should support them, but they are usually too busy seeking the truth to notice that it is being sabotaged behind their backs.

78.   THE SOKAL HOAX

Physics now enjoys such prestige that it is often used to confer respectability on quite unconnected subjects. Thus there are some writers who seek to bolster their speculations by mixing them with ill-understood concepts derived from quantum theory. This prostitution of science is not so easily identified by those without scientific training, and so it continues to flourish in certain quarters.

This was illustrated by the Sokal hoax. Alan Sokal, a physicist from New York University, wrote an article called "Transgressing the Boundaries: Towards a Transformation Hermeneutics of Quantum Gravity", and sent it to *Social Test*, a leading journal of cultural studies. This article purported to be a scholarly article about the postmodern philosophical and political implications of twentieth century physical theories. The editors, pleased that a distinguished physicist should contribute to their journal, willingly published the article, after it had been refereed by five members of the editorial board. It appeared in April 1996, in a special issue devoted to rebutting the criticism that journals of social studies often publish incompetent articles on science.

Sokal began by professing post-modernist beliefs. He poured scorn on scientists for clinging to the "dogma imposed by the long post-Enlightenment hegemony over the Western intellectual outlook", namely that there exists an external, objective world with properties independent of human beings, and that we can obtain reliable, though inevitably partial knowledge of these properties "by hewing to the 'objective' procedures and epistemological strictures prescribed by the (so-called) scientific method". Such dogmas, he maintains, have been completely discredited by the theories of general relativity and quantum mechanics. Physical reality is nothing but a "social and linguistic construct", as has been established by Bohr and Heisenberg. Quantum gravity, according to Sokal's essay, goes much further, supporting the post-modern denials of objective truth, but also initiating a truly liberating physics that would serve progressive causes. To illustrate this, he generates political conclusions from the physics of the very small. From Bohr's observation that in quantum mechanics "a complete elucidation of one and the same object may require diverse points of view" he concludes that "the content and methodology of postmodern science thus provides powerful intellectual support for the progressive political project, understood in its broadest sense: the transgressing of boundaries, the breaking down of barriers, the radical democratization of all aspects of social, economic political and cultural life."

The author later revealed in the journal *Lingua France* that "his essay was merely a farrago of deliberate solecisms, howlers and non-sequiturs, stitched together so as to look good and to flatter the ideological preconceptions of the editors." The sociologists were furious and the physicists were delighted. Now it was obvious to all that relativistic theories of truth are widely influential in certain purportedly academic circles, and that this has had devastating effects on the standards of scholarship and intellectual integrity.

It is worth enquiring why Sokal's article was accepted. Either the editors understood the article, or they did not. It is difficult to believe that they even thought that they understood what everyone else recognises as nonsense. The only other conclusion is that they did not care whether or not they understood it or not, so long as its conclusions supported their own ideology. They were glad to have a physicist supporting them, bringing with him all the prestige of the exact sciences, even if they could not understand what he was saying. Thus ideological criteria are to them more important than objective scholarly standards, or even sheer intelligibility.

79.   LAWS OF GOD AND CHURCH, MAN AND NATURE

There are, broadly speaking, four types of laws, and they have instructive similarities and differences that illustrate the relation between religion and science. First of all there are the laws of God and of the Church, given to regulate our conduct. God's laws are the Ten Commandments given by God to Moses on Mount Sinai which are absolute and can never be changed. The laws of the Church, such as the regulations for fasting and Mass observance, may be changed by the Pope or the bishops according to the circumstances. Since we have free-will, we can choose to disobey these laws and by so doing we bring upon ourselves, and often on others, suffering and punishment.

The laws of man are to be found in the legal system established by the state for the right ordering of human society. They often overlap the moral laws, but are not identical with them. Killing the innocent after birth, for example, is both immoral and illegal, but there are other actions that are immoral but not illegal, such as abortions that satisfy certain legal restrictions.

As in the case of the laws of God and of the Church, we may disobey the laws of the state, and be punished if we are caught. There may be unjust laws that command actions which are immoral and we may in conscience disobey them, though we may have to suffer the consequences. It is right to protest against such laws, and urge that they be repealed.

The laws of nature are different in several respects. God created matter with certain definite properties, and each particle of matter behaves exactly according to the law of its nature. Matter has no free-will so it has no choice but to obey. We are free to respect or ignore these laws, but matter takes no notice of our choice. If we behave as if the laws of gravity does not exist and jump off a cliff, then we are liable to get hurt.

There are today many patterns of thought and modes of behaviour that seem to imply that the laws themselves are subject to our wills. We are told that scientists impose their ideas on nature, so that our knowledge is purely subjective. The actual experiences of scientists are quite contrary to this. Very often scientists try to fit their observations into an existing theory, and are eventually driven to recognise that this is impossible. The theory has to be changed or replaced, and that is how science advances. The laws of nature are objective; they were there before we were born and will be there long after we have gone, and it is our task as scientists to discover them.

In a similar way the laws of God are objective facts that cannot be changed. Not even the Pope can change them, and to complain that he does not change them to suit our convenience is like criticising a physicist for not changing the law of gravity.

Politicians are particularly prone to imagine that they can frame their policies without taking due account of the laws of physics. Some of them think, for example, that we can satisfy our energy needs by building windmills and solar collectors, which any physicist could tell them is simply ridiculous. It is possible to evade reality for a while, but in the end it will assert itself, and the reckoning will be the more devastating the longer it is postponed. It should be added, in fairness, that politicians are often subject to strong pressures by ill-informed public opinion, and it is extremely difficult for them to go against this pressure. They need the support of those who know the laws of nature if they are to take the hard decisions that are needed for our future well-being.

80.   DOUBT AND CERTAINTY

Teachers of physics and mathematics often have the experience of telling a student that the answer they have given is wrong, even if they have not worked through the problem in detail. They know the answer is wrong because it contradicts some very general law such as the conservation of energy or momentum, or violates some symmetry principle. The student may protest that the answer he found comes from a computer calculation, but to no avail. We just tell him to go away and think again and, sure enough, he quite soon comes and says that he has found the mistake in his calculation. In such cases we can be sure because it is almost impossible for such general principles to be violated and, if they were, this would not be discovered by a student. I say almost impossible because there are some cases when even very general laws have been modified; thus the law of the conservation of energy has been replaced by the law of conservation of mass-energy, and the symmetry principle called parity conservation is sometimes violated.

We often believe things because they seem obvious, but they later turn out to be false. For centuries it was believed that the earth is immobile, and the sun, planets and stars move around it. It seems obvious that the earth is stationary, and indeed this can be supported by very plausible arguments. Thus if the earth is moving around the sun, the apparent positions of the stars would move with the seasons due to parallax, which is not observed. If the earth is rotating, the wind would blow everything to pieces and we would all fly off. Aristotle's belief in a stationary earth indeed accounts for commonsense observations better than the idea of Copernicus who said that the earth moves round the sun. It is only when precise and rather difficult measurements are made that the belief in a moving earth was ultimately vindicated, and the fallacies in the contrary arguments explained.

About a hundred years ago my grandfather believed that men would never fly. "It stands to reason," he would say, "that flying is impossible because men are heavier than air." Such experiences teach us that it is often difficult to find the truth.

It very frequently happens that people are quite sure that something is wrong, but they are unable to give any reasons for their belief. Contrary arguments are simply dismissed. This is the case for "politically correct" beliefs that are widespread today.

This is no new thing; it has always been difficult to accept novelties. When railway trains were first built, there was strong opposition because people expected that trains travelling at the unheard of speed of fifteen miles per hour, belching smoke and flame, would cause cows in nearby fields to drop dead with fright. Eventually, as Stephenson predicted, the railways became the great highways of the world.

When the first ships were built of iron instead of wood, people said that they would sink because iron is heavier than water, but they were soon proved wrong.

A contemporary example is the belief that nuclear power is unacceptably bad. This is so widespread that its further development is excluded. The arguments in its favour are not even discussed.

It is important to see how some beliefs that are eventually proved to be wrong come to be so widely accepted. In some cases, such as the belief that the sun moves around the earth and that parity is conserved, they are held because they seem to be common sense. In other cases, such as the unacceptability of nuclear power, they are the result of a sustained and powerful propaganda campaign.

81.   LANGUAGE IN RELIGION AND SCIENCE

There is a story that the Chinese sage Confucius was once asked what should be done in a time of crisis. He replied that the first task is to clean up the language. The language we use is the way we communicate with each other, and if the language is misleading, so will be the ideas, and then so will be the actions. If we keep our eyes open, we can find many examples where language is misused so as to insinuate ideas without stating them openly or providing any evidence for them. Thus I have heard Fr Jaki, the well known theologian-scientist, described as "controversial". When I challenged the speaker for an explanation, none was forthcoming. So I provided the explanation: he is controversial because he is outspoken in his support for the Papacy and the Magisterium. Liberal Catholics do not like this, but they do not say so openly.

"Censorship" is an emotion-charged word that is used immediately anyone proposes to curb or correct any dangerous activities or ideas. It conjures up the image of a stern humourless figure denying us our legitimate freedom and preventing access to enjoyment or knowledge. Indeed censors can sometimes act like this, but at present freedom often means licence. I do not want the food I buy to contain poisonous substances that will do harm without my realising it, so I am grateful to the inspectors who impose checks and controls to prevent this happening. I like to see a label on what I buy saying that its manufacture has been carefully controlled. Likewise I do not want the books I read to contain poisonous ideas that I might not recognise and could harm me, so I like to see the *Imprimatur*. This leaves my freedom intact; I can still eat or read poisonous rubbish if I so decide, but if I do so I have only myself to blame for the outcome.

I would therefore prefer newspapers and journals to say clearly at the head of their articles what are the beliefs of the writers; whether for example they are Catholics or Muslims or Anglicans, with perhaps some indication whether they are conservative or liberal. Then we would know where they stand. I have a friend in Oxford who would be accurately described as an evangelical atheist who says openly that his aim in life is to destroy the false ideas that infest my head. I appreciate his openness, and as we know just where we stand we can have a good discussion.

The emotionally-charged debate about energy and environment provides many instances of loaded language. We read about the "dumping" of radioactive waste, a word that insinuates the idea that it is done carelessly with no thought of the consequences. The word "disposal" would be more accurate. The methods of energy generation by wind, wave and solar are described as the "benign renewables", whereas statistical studies show that they are comparatively dangerous. Furthermore, there is no particular virtue in being renewable; what we need is a source that will be available for the foreseeable future. Another phrase that is gaining currency is "green energy", meaning energy generated by the "benign renewables" that are believed by some environmentalists to be the least destructive of the environment. More careful consideration shows, however, that these energy sources are not only unable to provide energy in the quantities and with the reliability we need, but would cover the land with wind turbines and solar panels, and the coastlines with huge wave machines.

It is not only words that can convey ideas; pictures can be even more effective. An advertisement for some product showing a white-coated scientist holding up a test-tube conveys the idea that the product is scientifically respectable. Similarly an advertisement showing a tough manly figure smoking a cigarette encourages smoking, while concealing the dangers. It is wise to look at what lies behind the words and the pictures.

82. BLIND SPOTS

Most of us have our blind spots. These are not just activities such as playing bridge or golf, or collecting bottle tops, that are quite familiar but are of no interest to us personally. We can understand and accept that they are of absorbing interest to other people and are quite happy to let them get on with it so long as they do not interfere with our own interests. Blind spots are much more radical than that: they are areas of thought that are completely absent. We do not know that they even exist, and when people try to tell us about them their words make no sense to us at all.

Some of these blind spots are relatively small and unimportant, at least most of us. In this category comes subtleties of Choctaw grammar, the rules of *ma jong* or the geometry of hyperspace. Others are of great and sometimes vital importance, and we are gravely impoverished if we have them. They may be due to our genes, or perhaps to our upbringing, but they permanently impoverish our lives. They are even found in highly intelligent people.

It is difficult for those without a particular blind spot to make any meaningful contact with those who have it. It is increasingly clear that a very prevalent blind spot is the whole area of religious belief. In previous centuries religious beliefs were often fiercely disputed. In the early Church everyone recognised that it is of overriding importance to have the correct beliefs concerning the natures of Christ and His relations to the other Persons of the Trinity. Voices were raised in the market place, and preachers who said the wrong thing were howled down by unruly mobs. Nowadays accounts of such scenes are received with incredulity. Whatever was all the fuss about? Who cares anyway? You can believe whatever you like; it means nothing to me. Thus the greatest danger the Church has to face is not persecution but indifference. We believe that we possess vital truths, but there are few who listen. It is no use having great knowledge if we cannot convey it to those who need to know.

Another prevalent blind spot is mathematics. We all realise that we have to make simple arithmetical calculations, but this can be done with computers. If, after buying several items, one quietly puts the total sum due onto the counter, the shop assistant, when she has eventually reached the total using her computer, is astonished. "How did you do that?" she exclaims, obviously thinking that one is in league with the devil.

More seriously, there are important public discussions that absolutely require some knowledge of quantitative measurements. Without this knowledge, one cannot say anything that makes any useful sense. There are people who passionately oppose nuclear radiations who know nothing about how they are measured. If you told them that they had just received a dose of one microsievert, they would not know whether to laugh or to call a priest to give them the last rites. They declare that all radioactive discharges should be forbidden, apparently not knowing that their own bodies contain radioactive potassium.

One might think that they would be glad to know more, that they would welcome some information about such subjects. Astonishingly, this is seldom the case. One just meets a blank wall, a blind spot. Whatever one says makes no impression at all.

In science, as in religion, there are people with blind spots who do not know, who do not know that they do not know, and who do not even know what knowing means.

83.   THE SPIRITUAL VALUE OF MATHEMATICS

Mathematics, in one form or another, enters our lives in many ways. We first encounter it as a subject at school, which we either enjoy or hate. Even before that, our parents have taught us to count, and we have to learn to add and subtract when we buy things in shops. Later on, we begin to learn geometry, algebra and trigonometry, and some years later the differential and integral calculus.

The study of mathematics is a valuable training in rigorous thinking. We are faced by a problem, and we know that there is only one correct answer. Often we have to think very hard to find the best way to solve it. We know that there is a way, and we must find it. This is a good preparation for tackling the more difficult problems of life; these may not have a simple answer, but still it is essential to tackle them in an objective and logical way.

When he was an undergraduate at Oxford, mathematics was Cardinal Newman's principal subject, and this is very likely the reason why his writings are so clear and logical, and have stood the test of time. He knew very well that the important thing is to get the answer right, irrespective of any personal or emotional feelings, and so he did not hesitate to leave the Church of England as soon as he was convinced that the Catholic Church is the One True Fold, a phrase to be found in all the letters he wrote to his relatives and friends on the eve of his reception.

Mathematics is also essential if we are to find to right answers to the many problems that face our society today. An obvious example is the choice of the best energy source to provide the heat and power we need for our homes, transport and industries. We need a source that is powerful enough to do the job, reliable, safe, cheap and environmentally benign. Most of these criteria can be expressed numerically, and it is essential to do so before we make any decisions. If we do not do this, then we are at the mercy of political pressure groups, emotion and propaganda.

Also essential for modern life is some understanding of the branch of mathematics called statistics. Most of our decisions have to be based on probabilities, so it is important to know what they are, and how to assess them. How many people, for example, would we have to interview before we can say that 10% of the population have decided to vote for a different party?

Politicians are notoriously unable to think statistically. They say, for example, that they will not approve a new energy source or food until it is proved to be perfectly safe, when they should know that energy sources and foods are never perfectly safe. What they should do is to list the various energy sources and foods and give the probabilities of harm and leave it to people to make up their own minds. The trouble with this, as they know quite well, is that no one will understand what they are talking about. If, however, they do not even try to explain the relative risks, then no one will ever learn.

Every day we do things that carry an element of risk. We cross the road, drive the car and eat food. Even walking along the pavement carries some risk. We cannot avoid such risks, but what we can do is to reduce them as far as reasonably possible. What happens all too often is that people worry about quite minuscule risks and think nothing of taking much more serious ones. This could be avoided by statistical studies.

Unfortunately, just as mathematics is needed more than ever before, the general knowledge of simple mathematics is declining. The widespread use of hand calculators is producing a generation that is incapable of the simplest arithmetical operations, and this inevitably breeds innumeracy and insensitivity to the importance of numerical assessment to find the best approach to serious social and moral problems.

84. ECLIPSES

The time is happily long past when it was believed that eclipses were portents of coming disaster, and prayers and sacrifices were offered to prevent the moon eating the sun. This is an example of the value of science in destroying superstitious beliefs.

Eclipses have been recorded from ancient times. The Chinese records go back well beyond 1000 BC, and the Babylonians made particularly accurate observations. The Chinese and Babylonian records have been particularly useful in establishing the chronology of ancient times.

The Muslims established many observatories from Spain to Iraq that flourished from the 8th to the 12th centuries, and the timing of the eclipses was used to estimate the distances between cities. There is an old tradition that a solar eclipse took place just after the death of the Prophet Mohammad's infant son. This was interpreted by some Muslims as a sign of sorrow in the heavens, but the Prophet very sensibly told them that it was just a coincidence.

Now that we understand the motions of the planets and the moon, we know that eclipses occur when the sun, the moon and the earth are in a straight line, and the times when this happens can be calculated very precisely from Newton's dynamics. We know, years in advance, just when an eclipse will occur, the zones of total and partial eclipse, and how it will look at any place as a function of the time. This is in sharp contrast with weather prediction, which frequently fails even for very short times. The reason for this difference is that eclipses depend on the motions of just three bodies, whereas the weather depends so sensitively on a very large number of variables in a way that makes reliable prediction impossible.

There is one very curious feature of eclipses, namely that the apparent sizes of the sun and the moon are the same. This makes it possible to see the sun's corona during a total eclipse. If the apparent size of the moon were less than that of the sun, there would be always at least a ring of brightness, so that the corona would not be visible. If it were greater, the corona also would be obscured. Why is the fit so exact? There is no scientific explanation, and indeed the coincidence is only temporary, because the distance of the moon from the earth is slowly increasing, and hence its apparent diameter is slowly decreasing.

Another remarkable feature of the moon is that it always looks the same. As it goes round the earth, it also rotates so that we see only the same face. The other side of the moon is only known through observations from artificial satellites. Is this yet another remarkable coincidence? In this case the answer is no. The rotation of the moon is due to tidal forces that ensure that the same hemisphere is always facing the earth. Such forces would have no effect on a perfectly spherical moon, so this tells us that the moon is slightly non-spherical, like the earth itself.

Solar eclipses have been very important in the history of science because they provide rare opportunities to see the stars near the sun. During a total eclipse the stars near the sun are easily seen, and their positions can be measured and compared with their usual positions. If there is any difference it shows that the starlight has been deflected as it passed near the sun, and this is interpreted as due to the action of gravity on the starlight. It was the solar eclipse of 1919 that was observed in the island of Principe, in the Gulf of Guinea in Brazil that made it possible for Arthur Eddington to measure the bending of starlight by the sun, and hence verify Einstein's theory of general relativity.

So why did God decide that the moon should during our times be at the right distance from the earth to make total solar eclipses possible? Perhaps He just wanted to make it easy for us to verify Einstein's theory.

THE CHURCH AND SCIENCE

85.   HOPES FOR THE MILLENNIUM

Science in the Life of the Church

It is always hazardous to look into the seeds of time, but hope is not prophecy and so we cannot be faulted if our hopes are unrealised. Nevertheless, if hope is to be realistic it must be based on solid fact and, whatever may happen in the next millennium, it seems almost certain that science and technology will play an even more important part than they did in the millennium just ending.

So it is vital that the Church takes full account of the possibilities and dangers of science and technology. This is not only in the superficial sense of making use of technology in its work of spreading the Gospel, but in the more fundamental sense of being fully aware of the ideas and methodologies of science itself, and being alert to the likely effects of new technological developments on our lives and activities.

Science has profoundly altered the way we think about the world, and this affects our thoughts in many ways. We now know that we live on a relatively small blue ball orbiting the sun, itself a rather ordinary star on one of the spiral arms of a vast galaxy of stars, and that this galaxy is but one of many billions of such galaxies. The traditional teaching about heaven and hell, the Ascension and the Assumption, were easy to interpret in terms of a fixed earth at the centre of the world, but how should we think about them now?

The Word of God is given to us in the Bible, which speaks to us in everyday language, not the language of science, and this leads many to reject its teaching. It is easy to say that the Bible teaches us the way to heaven, not the way the heavens go, but there still remains the cosmology that lies behind many Biblical passages, a cosmology that is now superseded. The Galileo affair still casts a long shadow, despite his recent rehabilitation, and inclines theologians to be wary of science. They are not reassured by the secularist and anti-theological tone of many popular scientific writers. We may indeed be confident that the Church will not make the same mistake again. As Newman remarked: "that past controversy and its issue have taught me beyond mistake that men of the greatest theological knowledge may firmly believe that scientific conclusions are contrary to the word of God when they are not so, and pronounce that to be heresy which is truth. It has taught me that Scripture is not inspired to convey mere secular knowledge, whether about the heavens or the earth, or the race of men; and I need not fear for Revelation, whatever truths may be brought to light by means of observation and experience out of the world of phenomena which environ us."

Nevertheless, the malaise remains, and it is apparent in many ways. There is a cultural gap between theology and natural science, so that theologians in the 19th and 20th centuries saw science mainly as a source of trouble, as an invader to be driven back to its methodological domain, rather than as an ally from whom something can be learned. The teaching in Catholic schools and colleges is on the whole more strongly weighted than it should be to the humanities, to the relative neglect of science. There are many excellent Catholic scientists, but not as many as one might expect. Catholic newspapers and periodicals devote very little space to scientific and technological concerns, and in many controversial questions such as the energy crisis they tend to adopt uncritically the errors and exaggerations of the mass media, instead of seeking the truth and publicising it.

What then are the grounds for hoping that this situation will improve? First of all, we are blessed with a Pope who looks to the future with hope and confidence, and who also has a strong interest in science. When he was in Cracow he held regular discussions on scientific matters, and in numerous addresses he has shown how highly he values science and technology and how he recognises its importance in our lives. He is supported by the Pontifical Academy of Sciences that holds many meetings on scientific and technological questions, and publishes the conclusions. This work is of the greatest value, but it is not well publicised and so never reaches the Church as a whole. We may hope that this situation will be soon rectified.

The bishops are well placed to ensure that the words of the Pope are heeded and that science is brought into the life of the Church. To be effective, the bishops need the collaboration of scientists, since they are able to provide their specialised knowledge. Already several hierarchies have shown their recognition of the importance of such work. Thus the bishops of the United States have published detailed studies of particular questions, such as that on energy questions in 1981. The English and Welsh bishops have urged that "the Church must draw into the work of evangelisation those Catholics who have an acknowledged competence in contemporary scientific disciplines." Scientific questions are now covered in many seminary courses: the work of Fr Michael Sharratt, making use of the Galileo case, is an outstanding example.

In order that Catholic scientists may serve the Church they need also to have some understanding of philosophy and theology, and this in turn requires teachers familiar with these disciplines. It is not easy to attain a sufficient knowledge of all three, since any one of them can easily absorb a lifetime. Those most favourably placed are those who have spent the first part of their lives studying science, and have subsequently entered the religious life. They thus have both the basic scientific training, and the philosophical and theological knowledge. The need for such theologians has been explicitly emphasised by the Pope. They are then able to show, by word and by their writings, how Catholic scientists and seminarians and teachers can play their full part in the life of the Church in the third millennium.

That is our hope for the future.

86.   SCIENTISTS IN ROME

An International Conference on Faith and Science was held in Rome on 23rd and 24th May 2000 as part of the Jubilee celebrations. The Conference provided an opportunity for scientists from many countries to meet and discuss contemporary problems concerning philosophy, science and faith and to consider the outlook for the third millennium.

The Conference began with an introductory address by Cardinal Poupard, the President of the Pontifical Council for Culture, followed by sessions devoted to a general consideration of philosophy, theology and science and then to more specialised problems. Many of the lectures were given by scientists who subsequently became priests such as Professor Tanzella-Nitti, an astronomer who is now professor of fundamental theology at the Pontifical University of the Holy Cross in Rome, and Professor Michael Heller, an astronomer who teaches in the Pontifical Academy in Cracow, Poland. This ensured that the discussions were well informed both in science and in theology.

The next session was chaired by Professor N. Cabibbo, the President of the Pontifical Academy of Sciences. I was asked to give an introductory meditation at the beginning of the session devoted to the natural sciences, and this was followed by lectures by Fr Michael Heller on "Faith and Reason", Professor Robert Russell from the Centre for Theology and the Natural Sciences in Berkeley on "Creation and Big Bang and Quantum Cosmologies" and finally by Professor Edward Nelson from Princeton University on "Mathematics and Faith".

This was followed by a session on "The Science of Man and Life", with lectures on medicine and man, human ecology, artificial intelligence and the mind-body relation. Finally there was a session on the social sciences with a lecture on "Faith and the Concept of Humanity in the Social Sciences" by Margaret Archer of the University of Warwick and a member of the Pontifical Academy of Social Sciences.

The concluding address was given by the Archbishop of Lublin, Josef Zycinski, who was formerly professor of the philosophy of science at the Pontifical Academy in Cracow, on "New Perspectives for the Relationship between Science and Faith in the Light of *Fides et Ratio*". The lectures and discussions will be published as a book.

After the Conference, the participants attended a Penitential Liturgy, a Celebration of the Eucharist and Profession of Faith, and finally an audience with the Holy Father in St Peter's. The scientists first processed through the Holy Door and then down the nave to the seats reserved near the altar. The Mass was said by Cardinal Poupard, with readings in Italian and English, and prayers in another eight languages. When the Mass was completed the lights went up still further and the Holy Father entered and came down the nave, acknowledging greetings from the assembled crowds. Arriving at the altar, he walked up the steps unaided and sat on a throne in front of the altar. Cardinal Poupard then reported on the conference to the Pope, who replied with an address in Italian, French, English and Spanish. The scientists were then invited to come up one by one to meet the Holy Father. We knelt to kiss his ring and he held our hands in his in a gesture that said more than words. He conveys to everyone that you are the person he specially wants to meet and that you are a person of infinite value. That is the most valued impression that remains from a meeting that also provided much food for thought and action in the third millennium.

87. THE PLACE OF SCIENTISTS IN THE LIFE OF THE CHURCH

In September 1998 a conference organised by *Pax Romana*, the international association of Catholic graduates, was held in the All Saints Pastoral Centre, St Albans. It included a day arranged by the International Secretariat for Scientific Questions on the theme "The Place of the Scientist in the Life of the Church".

This theme was chosen because we believe that science and its associated technology has an all-pervasive influence on our modern society; indeed it is largely responsible for making it what it is. At the same time there is much secularist propaganda saying that religion is a thing of the past that has been replaced by science. This can unsettle young people and even cause them to leave the Church.

Relations between theologians and scientists have not always been good, for various reasons. Theologians have sometimes opposed new scientific discoveries and scientists have reacted with ridicule. The theological and scientific cultures have diverged, and during the last two centuries theologians have tended to regard science mainly as a source of trouble that should be kept firmly within its methodological limits and not as an ally to be welcomed. There was little realisation among them that science tells us about God's world and can assist the development of theology. Scientists therefore have a positive role to play in the life of the Church, and the Science Secretariat Day was arranged to develop this theme.

We had six lecturers, and two more sent written contributions. The first lectures, by Fr Joseph Tanzella-Nitti (an astronomer now lecturing on theology in Rome) and Fr Manuel Doncel SJ (an elementary particle physicist now lecturing on the philosophy of science in Barcelona). A written contribution was received from Fr J. Sanguineti (Rome). They examined the relation of science to theology, and showed that theologians must take into account the modern knowledge of the universe and its evolution. This is particularly important when interpreting the Bible. This work is supported by the Pope who welcomes science, respects its autonomy and encourages its development.

Catholic scientists have a responsibility to develop their knowledge of their Faith and its relations with theology, so that they can play their part in the life of the Church. Education at all levels, schools, colleges, universities and seminaries is vitally important. Professor Derkse (a chemist and philosopher) gave an account of his teaching of philosophy from a Catholic viewpoint at the Technical University of Eindhoven, and the Abbé Magnin (a physicist) described courses in French seminaries. Fr Michael Sharratt (a philosopher) sent a written contribution describing how he taught the seminarians at Ushaw College to understand science itself, its philosophy and its relation to theology by means of a detailed study of the Galileo case.

Scientific matters are rarely covered in the Catholic Press. There are few articles on science for its own sake and hardly any well-chosen book reviews. Mr John Wilkins (editor of the *Tablet*) explained his viewpoint, stressing that he has to respond to the public misgivings about science. Finally, the Honorary President Professor Lucien Morren (a physicist), still active in his tenth decade, spoke on the mission of the Catholic scientist: to study, to teach, to serve the Church and society, and to praise God for His creation.

It was a very full day, with many useful discussions. The full texts of the lectures have been published. They contain much food for thought and ideas for action, and should encourage Catholic scientists to play their full part in the life of the Church.

88.   IRRELEVANT?

It has been astutely observed that the main threat to the Church is not persecution but just being considered irrelevant. Most people no longer think that the Christian Faith has any relevance to them. The story of the Passion and Death of Christ is regarded in much the same way as accounts of Aztec ceremonies, doubtless interesting as an example of comparative mythology, but of course quite irrelevant to the way we live. All religions should be tolerated, because they are all just opinions. The very idea of objective truth has vanished. The idea that there is a moral law that we must obey at our peril is simply preposterous. We know nothing about life after death, so let us make the most of the life we have.

This view of religion is mirrored by a view of science that has now become widespread. All is relative and socially conditioned. Scientists disagree among themselves so nothing they say can be trusted. We must care about the environment, but how we do it is to be decided by emotion and rhetoric.

Many of the current discussions in the Church have been likened to rearranging the deck chairs on the *Titanic*. Time is wasted discussing subjects that have been definitively settled. The teaching of the Magisterium, that could bring some much-needed sense, is ignored or undermined. The Catholic press is filled with accounts of matters of minor importance and reviews of marginal books. Eminent clerics smilingly assure us that all is well with the Church, when it is obvious that it is not: great seminaries lie empty, several religious orders are in terminal decline and a large proportion of the products of our grammar schools lapse as soon as they leave.

What is to be done about this? There are no easy answers, but an important start can be made by facing the truth. First of all the truth about our Faith, not watered down or adapted to soothe modern feelings. The life of Christ has become so familiar that it fails to shock us into changing our lifestyles. Then the truth about the state of the Church. Finally the truth about the world we live in.

Failure to face the truth is evident in most of the media discussions about the future of our society. Partly this is due to a reluctance to change anything, and partly because in many matters the truth can be found only by a careful scientific analysis, and that means putting numbers to things wherever possible. Many, if not most, people dislike numbers, and prefer to try to settle things by qualitative arguments. The editors of newspapers and periodicals know that people dislike numbers, and so they generally refuse to publish numerical analyses, and as a result it is impossible to ascertain the truth. People then worry about relatively unimportant things while ignoring real dangers. The Government organises conferences on urgent problems and considers a range of possible solutions except the one that a slight acquaintance with the numbers shows is the most important. In spite of this, numbers are considered irrelevant.

It is easy to give examples of this folly. How can we decide if the radiations around Sellafield are harmful without knowing the results of measurements? How can we decide which are the best energy sources to use without numerical estimates of their capacity, cost, reliability and safety? Will global warming cause a rise in the sea level? Unless one is thoroughly familiar with the best numerical estimates and their likely margins of uncertainty it is not possible even to begin a sensible discussion of such questions. Very often there are powerful political forces that impose decisions that are demonstrably harmful to society. Scientists are kept out of the debate because they might impede this process.

The Church has a great opportunity here. It is not hamstrung by political or economic considerations, and so is free to proclaim the objective truth.

89.   THE VOCATION OF THE CATHOLIC SCIENTIST

When we are asked to pray for vocations it is nearly always in connection with the priesthood or the religious life. Some men and women are indeed called by God to serve Him in these ways. But they are not the only ones; we are all called, in one way or another. Each of us has a specific vocation, a task planned by God that only we can perform. For most of us our vocation is to serve Him through our state of life, our professional activities, whether we are doctors or teachers, lawyers or accountants, parents or single people.

It is certainly true for scientists. Our first duty, as for all professionals, is to be a good scientist, to be fully equipped with the knowledge and skills necessary for us to carry out our duties. This requires many years of hard study at school and university, followed by additional training to prepare ourselves to enter the academic world, research institute or industry. In addition to carrying out the duties of our profession, there are also duties as members of the Church, duties that can only be carried out by scientists. To do this effectively requires a deeper understanding of science than that provided in most university courses, and to acquire this requires further study. This is more difficult than it may seem because it requires guidance that is seldom available.

Scientists can put their knowledge at the service of the Church in many ways. Science greatly affects modern society, and this raises new moral problems. Some of these affect us all, such as the protection of the environment, global warming, pollution, nuclear power and a whole range of medical advances. Pressure groups arise and urge action, and the Church is expected to have an answer. If the discussion is to be useful, it must be based on expert knowledge, and this can only be provided by the scientists who have studied the particular problem concerned. It is for the bishops to decide whether to make a statement, and they have indeed done so on many of the problems mentioned. If they are to make an effective statement, they need the support and advice of scientists. It is not easy to make a statement that is both accurate scientifically and correct morally, as shown by many instances based on inadequate scientific study. Very often the amount of scientific knowledge required is seriously underestimated, as if complex problems can be solved on the basis of general principles and a few half-truths obtained from the media. Quite often some issue arises unexpectedly, and it can only be addressed adequately by someone who has studied it for years, and has all the relevant information at his or her fingertips.

The media provide a wider scope for the scientist. Controversies arise, often initiated by a secular scientist pouring scorn in the name of science on some aspect of Christian belief, and these need to be answered by a believing Christian who is scientifically qualified. One might have expected that the contributions of qualified scientists to the media debate would be welcomed, but in general this is not so. Pressure groups have their own agenda, and do not want to be contradicted. It requires considerable persistence to make any impression on this situation, which is of considerable danger for our society. Scientists often have the experience of trying to correct obvious errors in a public discussion, only to have their attempts ignored, or contradicted without the opportunity of reply.

Some of the problems were considered during a meeting devoted to the place of the scientist in the life of the Church held at St Albans in 1998. The lectures given on that day have now been published.

90.   SCIENTIFIC LITERACY

Our lives are increasingly affected by science and technology. Scientific discoveries and ideas are frequently described and discussed in the media, and the applications of science are all around us. They have changed our lives in many ways inconceivable to people living just a few decades ago.

These applications of science are not all benign: if they have many advantages and improve the quality of our lives, they often have other effects that we want to avoid. Our cars provide an easy means of transport, and yet many lives are lost by accidents. The same may be said for other means of transport. Technology thus raises many serious ethical questions that are frequently debated in the media. How do we control technology to make it safer without curtailing our freedom? We all think that we should have a say in the discussions of such questions, and yet we realise that this often requires scientific knowledge that few people have. It is not practicable for everyone to study science to a high level, and yet how can we all participate in such discussions?

What is needed is not a specialised knowledge of science, but what may be called scientific literacy. This is quite different from scientific knowledge, and needs to be taught in schools to everyone, not just to those specialising in science. By scientific literacy is meant a general background knowledge of science and how it interacts with human concerns.

Some examples may make this clearer. We all need to know how scientific knowledge is obtained by careful observation and controlled experimentation, what are the things that can go wrong and how the results can be verified. This in turn needs some knowledge of statistics, so that we can answer questions like "how many people have to be interviewed in order to establish that there has been a 5% increase in support for a particular party?" If we read a discussion about nuclear radiations we need to know how they are measured, and that we are all the time exposed to the natural background radiation. This provides a point of reference, so we can ask how the source under discussion compares with the background level. In all these discussions, if a thing can be measured, then it must be measured before we can draw any sensible conclusions.

Many contemporary discussions presuppose some scientific knowledge, and without this knowledge the discussions do not make sense. Thus archaeology makes use of carbon dating, dendrochronology, thermoluminescence and many other techniques. We do not need to know about them in detail, so that we could do them ourselves, but we do need to know what they mean and how they work.

Modern medicine uses a wide variety of scientific techniques for diagnosis and treatment, such as ultrasound, radiation therapy, chemotherapy, nuclear magnetic resonance, isotope tracers, pacemakers, genetic modification, X-rays and gamma ray cameras, and we need to know in general how they work if we are to understand what is being done to us.

It is useful to know something about the universe we live in. What is the Big Bang and how do we know about it? Why is it hot in summer and cold in winter, and why are the seasons different in Australia? How do we know that the earth moves round the sun? What are cosmic rays and meteorites? How does a satellite keep up?

Most of us drive our cars without much thought about how the engine works. What are the signs of malfunction or danger? When is the road likely to be slippery and what can we do about it?

You may think that all such knowledge is obvious; you do not have to be taught it, you just keep you eyes open and your brain in gear. Fine, you are scientifically literate!

91. EMOTION OR REASON?

The acquittal of the Greenpeace protesters shows once again the way our society is going. They expressed their opposition to genetic modification by destroying a substantial area where such crops were being tested. They were acquitted, it seems, because the members of the jury were more concerned to support their campaign than to apply the law. It was argued that the law does allow destructive acts in emergencies, but that would hardly apply in this case.

This prompts several reflections. First there is the spiral downward into violence: if you can destroy my property and go unpunished, why cannot I do the same to you? Then there is an implicit attack on reason. Our society is faced with many difficult decisions, and strong passions are aroused. Intuition may sometimes be right, but in general the only sensible way is to consider the reasons as carefully as possible and then come to a decision. Many scientific bodies have done this for genetic modification and have concluded that, with due precautions, this has great potential benefits. Trials have been authorised and are taking place. If one has objections, these should be carefully considered by qualified people. To take the law into one's own hands is to overturn the card table and make further progress impossible.

This is continually happening. In the last few months there have been two articles in a well-known Catholic weekly on subjects related to science that seemed to me to be mistaken. Views were expressed without proper scientific justification. So I wrote to the authors asking them to explain the reasons for their views and also wrote to the journal. My letters were not answered and my arguments were brushed aside. What can I do next: throw a bomb through their window? No, that would be to deny all

I stand for and make further progress impossible. Yet it is appalling that there seemed to be no interest in examining the matter in order to find the truth. It is the truth that matters above all. It is highly dangerous to propagate untruths, and it is almost unbelievable that any right-minded person would willingly do so. If we make a mistake, the only honest and sensible thing to do is to correct it as speedily as possible. The whole affair was yet another example of the scandalously low level of scientific literacy in the Church.

In his recent address to university professors, the Holy Father emphasised that: "A culture without truth does not safeguard freedom but puts it at risk." On a previous occasion he said: "The demands of truth and morality neither degrade nor abolish our freedom, but on the contrary enable freedom to exist and liberate it from its own inherent threats."

At a higher level, the rejection of reason poses a threat to our Faith. In the same discourse the Holy Father went on: "We cannot be satisfied with an ambiguous reconciliation of the kind favoured by a culture which doubts the very ability of reason to arrive at the truth. This path runs the risk of *misconstruing faith by reducing it to a feeling,* to emotion, to art; in the end stripping faith of all critical foundation. But this would not be Christian faith, which demands instead a reasonable and responsible acceptance of all that God has revealed in Christ. *Faith does not sprout from the ashes of reason!* I strongly encourage all of you, men and women of the university, to spare no effort in rebuilding that aspect of learning which is open to Truth and the Absolute."

It all illustrates the sad truth that it is very difficult in these times for reason even to obtain a hearing, let alone influence events. As Newman remarked, "Quarry the granite rock with a razor, moor the vessel with a thread of silk, and then you may hope with such delicate instruments as human knowledge and human reason to contend against those giants, the passion and the pride of man."

SCIENCE AND SOCIETY

92. REFLECTIONS ON THE PAST MILLENNIUM

As the millennium approaches our thoughts naturally turn towards the future. We try, with varying success, to look into the seeds of time, to see which grains will grow and which will not. It is perhaps even more instructive to cast an eye on the millennium just ending and to try to identify some of the most momentous changes that have taken place in that period.

As the last millennium began, the period known as the Dark Ages was drawing to a close, and the High Middle Ages was dawning. This was arguably one of the most fruitful and innovative periods in recorded history. The thirteenth has been hailed as the greatest of centuries. It saw the building of great cathedrals and abbeys and the foundation of universities. The treasures of ancient Greek learning were becoming available through translations from the Arabic made principally in Spain. Scholars flocked to the new universities in Bologna, Padua, Paris and Oxford and struggled to understand Plato and Aristotle, and to see how their ideas and concepts could be used to express the Christian Faith with increasing precision. Albert the Great, Bonaventure and Aquinas used this heritage and built on the work of Jewish and Muslim philosophers and theologians to systematise theology and to put it on a firm rational basis.

At that time the view of the natural world was based on Aristotle, and this was widely accepted. Aristotle was greatly valued, but the medieval philosophers and theologians did not hesitate to reject his views if they departed from Christian orthodoxy. Aristotelian physics, based on a central stationary earth, and distinguishing between changeable terrestrial matter and unchanging celestial matter, had prevented the development of physics for nearly two thousand years. Gradually, the impact of Christian beliefs broke the stranglehold of Aristotelian physics and opened the way to modern science. In Paris, John Buridan thought about the problem of motion. The eternal universe of Aristotle was rejected as contrary to the Christian belief in creation, and Buridan surmised that God, when He created the world, gave each particle an impetus that kept it going without any further divine action, except that by which God keeps everything in existence. This was the germ of the concept of momentum, and Buridan's work was the critical breakthrough that made modern science possible.

From this small beginning came, in the fullness of time, the transformation of our lives through science and technology that is one of the most notable features of our millennium. "Not since the birth of a babe in a manger," wrote Whitehead, "was there such a change in human history as that due to the birth of science."

Science came to maturity in the Renaissance, with the work of Copernicus and Kepler, Galileo and Newton. For the first time in history it was possible to understand the natural world in a scientific way. From Newton's equations of motion, together with his theory of gravitation, it is possible to calculate with high precision the motions of the planets and those of terrestrial bodies. The Renaissance was marked also by great artistic achievements, but at the same time came the Reformation and the rise of Protestantism. Christianity was torn apart, and the unity of the Middle Ages shattered.

In the following centuries natural science entered a period of continual growth and the great voyages of discovery in the fifteenth and sixteenth centuries brought to Europe a whole new range of flora and fauna, as well as making Europeans conscious of civilisations very different from their own. The movement called the Enlightenment increasingly alienated Europeans from their Christian heritage and heightened the prestige of science.

By the nineteenth century the phenomena of electricity and magnetism had been described by Maxwell's equations, and the chemical structure of matter explored in depth. This scientific understanding of matter fused with the empirical knowledge of the workman and this greatly accelerated technological developments. The industrial revolution made possible the production in factories of a whole new range of goods at prices ensuring their wide distribution, and this in turn greatly improved living standards. Canals and then railways facilitated the transport of goods, and increased social mobility. The telephone and the electric telegraph made possible worldwide instantaneous communication.

The twentieth century brought even greater changes. The understanding of the natural world was revolutionised by Einstein's theories of relativity and gravitation, and by Planck's discovery of the quantum. Then Rutherford discovered the nucleus of the atom, and quantum mechanics made possible a detailed understanding first of the atom and then of the nucleus. In a few decades this made possible new technologies that brought radio, television, computers, mobile telephones into the hands of millions. Medicine made great strides. It conquered most killer diseases and made it possible to diagnose and treat injuries by X-rays, radioactive isotopes and nuclear radiations. Communication and travel was further facilitated by larger and faster aeroplanes.

At the same time, science and technology were also applied to war. Poison gas was used in the First World War, and the atomic bomb in the Second. The coal that fuelled the industrial revolution, and the oil that has superseded it for many applications, have polluted the atmosphere. The demand for energy increases, and the oil is running out. Nuclear power has the potential to provide the needed energy, but is hamstrung by political opposition.

During the present century, Christianity remains divided into Catholics, Protestants and Orthodox, and numerous small sects. Some flourish, and many are withering away. Protestantism is fragmenting and losing its fundamental beliefs. The Orthodox retain a deep spirituality but generally fail to engage the modern world. Catholicism has been shaken out of its complacency by the Vatican Council, and shows decline in some areas and renewed vitality in others. Relations between denominations are generally more friendly than before, and there is openness to Eastern religions. Europe is increasingly secular, though still living on its Christian capital. Many are concerned only with this life, and the pleasures it brings, and the larger framework of higher obligations and eternal destiny is a vanishing memory. Whether this trend will continue, or whether the new generation will perceive its shallowness, will be seen in the next millennium.

93. PERFECTLY SAFE?

Of course we want everything to be perfectly safe: anything that is not perfectly safe should be banned! Unfortunately life is not as simple as that; almost nothing is perfectly safe. We all know this very well in our everyday lives. We often have small accidents and sometimes serious ones. We know that it is not perfectly safe to cross the road, or even to walk along the pavement. We know that road accidents are tragically frequent. These accidents are more or less under our control in the sense that they are often our own fault, and we have come to terms with them.

It is a similar situation with other accidents where we are entirely in the hands of others, such as when we are on a ship or in a plane. We know that accidents sometimes happen, but we have come to terms with them as well. This is realistic and sensible. Obviously we must do all we can to reduce accidents to the minimum, but then we accept that some hazards remain.

What is much more serious is that in some other areas, we seem to have lost all sense of proportion, and become paranoid about relatively small dangers while remaining complacent about much larger ones. A prime example is the recent scare about beef and lamb. Quite properly, the government consults scientists about the risk of contracting disease from infected meat. In the circumstances, no scientist is going to say that it is perfectly safe, because there is a small chance of infection and he would be disgraced if someone did indeed succumb. So the scientists report to the government that there is a small danger. The Minister of Health then makes a speech saying that he is not going to approve the sale of any meat that carries any risk of infection, and bans the sale of such meat. Naturally the farmers are furious, and people find no meat in the shops. There is a deadly logic in this process, which if carried to extremes could lead to almost everything being banned.

In such circumstances, the Minister should have the courage to repeat the conclusions of the scientists, say that there is some small danger, and let people make up their own minds whether to take the risk or not. In addition, it is of course essential to see that the source of the infection is removed, and this may require legislation if the industry does not do it itself.

It is just the same with nuclear radiations. People have become so paranoid about the word "nuclear" that hospitals have re-named the diagnostic technique that used to be called nuclear magnetic resonance. There is a great fear of nuclear radiations, but almost no attempt to understand them. We have all been exposed to nuclear radiations all our lives. Some comes from radioactive materials inside our bodies, some from radioactive rocks and soil, some from the cosmic radiation and some from medical treatment. This is the background radiation, which no one has ever worried about. This background radiation varies by factors of ten or more from one place to another. In Cornwall it is about twice as high as the rest of the country, but this does not stop people going there for their holidays. The intensity of the cosmic radiation increases with altitude, so the higher you go the more you receive. Mountaineers never bother about this, and neither do people travelling by air. All these doses are so small that the deleterious effects, if any, are minuscule.

The situation changes dramatically when people hear that it is proposed to build a nuclear waste disposal site near their home. Immediately they are up in arms, and it is useless for the authorities to say that the amount of radioactivity is small and it will be buried so deep that it cannot harm anyone. Protest groups are formed and the MP for the area is worried. He tells the Minister that if this proposal goes ahead he will probably lose his seat in the next election. So the Minister decides to cancel the proposal.

94. THE COST OF SAFETY

The Paddington railway crash has once again focused public attention on the importance of safety. Newspaper headlines have demanded that safety take precedence over cost. It is very easy to make such demands, but not so easy to tackle the serious problems that underlie them.

The bitter truth that has to be faced is that nothing in this life is absolutely safe. It is living in a fool's paradise to demand perfect safety. Accidents continually happen: trains and aeroplanes crash, cars, buses and ships collide, oil rigs burst into flames, dams collapse, chemical plants explode and so on. Sometimes this is due to circumstances that no one can foresee, and sometimes they are due to carelessness, stupidity, ignorance and greed. In addition, there are natural disasters such as earthquakes and hurricanes that cannot be predicted and often have death tolls far greater than those due to man-made disasters.

Having said that, it is obviously necessary to make things as safe as reasonably possible. Then we come up against the second bitter truth that improved safety costs money, and there is only a limited amount available. If we spend more on safety, then there is less for education, health care, and many other urgent needs.

The same difficulties arise within each of these categories. Thus it is easy to say that medical care should be available to all, but does this include the most expensive operations and medicines? Since this is quite impracticable, hard choices have to be made, and even then the waiting lists continue to grow.

There is another more subtle reason why perfect safety is impossible, even if we were able to spend unlimited money. Safety equipment in factories, for example, has to be manufactured in other factories, and this itself involves further hazards. The result is that beyond a certain point improved safety in one area introduces a greater degree of hazard in another.

The only way to improve overall safety is to spend the available money so as to save as many lives as possible. This requires the collection of data concerning the cost of saving a life by each of the possible safety measures. There are many difficulties in this, but even approximate numbers are far better than no numbers at all.

This numerical approach is the best way to avoid emotional reactions to large spectacular accidents. Air crashes, rail crashes, mine collapses and dam failures that cause a large number of deaths simultaneously capture the headlines and lead to immediate demands for action, whereas a continuing series of much smaller accidents, such as those occurring daily on the roads, excites no such public comment. Yet if we look at the numbers over a period of time we can easily show that the total numbers of deaths on the roads are much larger than those associated with single spectacular accidents.

What we need is a list of the costs of saving lives in various ways, but we seldom see such figures. For example, I remember reading that a life can be saved by spending £5,000 on motorway crash barriers. At the other extreme, British Nuclear Fuels has spent £250,000,000 on reducing radioactive emissions that, on the worst (and probably false) assumption of a linear relation between dose and hazard, will save one life. Such figures show very clearly the glaring imbalances that exist, often due to the thoughtless actions of pressure groups. To avoid the loss of life these balances entail, we need similar figures for a wide range of other safety measures. This applies not only to man-made disasters, but to the precautions that should be taken to reduce the death tolls from natural disasters. Then we will be able to take realistic decisions that will save the most lives with the limited resources available.

95.   THE CONCORDE DISASTER

The crash of the French Concorde is a tragic reminder that however much care is taken with modern technology, we can never be sure that it is absolutely safe. The Concorde is a plane that was very carefully designed and made to high standards, is regularly tested and maintained, and until now has had an unsurpassed safety record, with no crashes in thirty years of operation. It has never been very successful commercially due to its high running costs, but for those who can afford to pay the high fares, it has become a very comfortable and convenient way to fly across the Atlantic and on other routes.

Such accidents are a feature of life, and they happen all the time. We recall the Paddington train disaster, the sinking of the *Herald of Free Enterprise*, the explosion of the chemical plant at Bhopal, the disaster of Chernobyl, the Lockerbie crash and a long series of accidents to oil rigs, dams and coal mines. In the period from 1969 to 1986 there were about 160 severe accidents, with death tolls of up to 2,500 people.

Our immediate reaction to the news of such a disaster is that we must make sure that it never happens again. Concorde must be grounded forever, nuclear power must be abandoned and so on. Calmer reflection leads to the realisation that such disasters are an inevitable feature of our modern technological society. Of course we must do all we can, within reason, to reduce their frequency but, as nothing is perfectly safe, they cannot be eliminated entirely. A further requirement is that we must use our limited resources to save as many lives as possible.

Spectacular disasters like the Concorde crash fill the front pages of newspapers and lead to demands for instant action, but the large number of smaller accidents with just a few casualties each, responsible for a much higher total number of deaths and injuries, receive much less publicity. The numbers killed on the roads are far greater than those killed in spectacular accidents. To save lives, it is much cheaper to install more motorway crash barriers than to ground Concorde. Another consideration is that safety devices themselves must be made, and this inevitably has its price in deaths and injuries.

Natural disasters like hurricanes, typhoons and floods, frequently claim hundreds of thousands of victims, and many of these lives could be saved by relatively simple precautions, On a longer term, there are the possible effects of global warming such as the flooding of low-lying areas and unpredictable climate changes. These are still uncertain, and probably will not be severe for some decades, but if and when they do occur the results may well be catastrophic.

In these circumstances, it is very difficult for governments to decide on the best strategy. The first step is to make careful statistical studies of many hazards, expressing the results numerically. This makes it possible to compare the numbers of deaths resulting from the activities listed above, and many others. The resulting numbers may not be very accurate, but it is far better to have imperfect numbers with known uncertainties than to have no numbers at all, and they enable governments to make informed decisions.

Tragically, this is not done. People seem to have lost all sense of proportion, becoming paranoid about relatively small dangers while remaining complacent about much larger ones. As a result, governments are subject to intense political pressure that forces them to take decisions that they know are not the best ones.

People demand perfect safety and so the politicians ask the scientists if an activity is perfectly safe. The scientists must then admit that although the new device or process is very safe and brings many benefits, it is not perfectly safe. The politicians can then respond either by telling people the truth and letting them take their own decisions, or they can take the matter into their own hands and ban the device or process.

The result of this is often to cause a greater loss of life because the benefits of the new activity are then not available.

96. ORGANISATIONAL FAILURE

The recent rail disaster at Hatfield has shown that there are several types of accidents. Some of them, like the Concorde crash and the Windscale reactor fire, are due to unforseen and probably unforeseeable events: an extremely rare set of circumstances in the former case and a hitherto unknown physical effect (the Wigner release) in the latter. All we can do in such circumstances is to make sure that they never happen again.

There is another type of disaster due to defects in organisation. This occurs when there is a well-understood and foreseeable set of circumstances that indicate the likelihood of a disaster, and yet due to organisational defects no action is taken. In the case of a railway accident, it is known that a defective rail can cause an accident and it may also be known that a particular rail is defective. However, the railways are under continual public pressure to keep the trains running on time. To replace the defective rail, some trains have to be cancelled to allow the defective rail to be replaced by a sound one. The resulting delays anger the passengers and the cancellation loses revenue. There is thus a strong pressure to postpone the repair. This may also be inevitable if not enough men are employed to carry out the necessary repairs. The fault is then with the organisation that tolerates insufficient staffing levels and so is unable to carry out frequent track inspections and to react quickly when a defective rail is found.

It is too early to say definitely that the Hatfield disaster falls into this category, but there are other examples such as the *R101* and *Challenger* disasters. The latter is fresh in our memory and has been extensively studied. It is well known that rocket launches are inherently hazardous as there are so many things that can go wrong. It became the practice to approve a launch when the conditions were similar to those of previous successful launches. As Richard Feynman remarked, this is rather like a mother who lets a child run across the road because he has already done this several times without mishap. The *Challenger* case was worse than this: it was known that the rubber seals between sections of the rocket were unreliable when the temperature was below 53 degrees, and yet on the day of the launch it was only 29 degrees.

The psychological pressures were intense. The schedule of possible launching times was very tight, and NASA wanted a successful launch to support their planned future programme. The President was due to talk live to the astronauts during the flight, as part of an important speech. As a result, political pressure overcame technical misgivings and the launch took place. The disaster was thus an institutional failure, not a technical failure. There was no one in the organisation with the power and the courage to cancel the launch.

An engineer with misgivings is in an almost impossible situation. If he makes his doubts known he will be very unpopular, and even his job may be at stake. He may be wrong in his assessment, and if he is overridden and the launch then takes place successfully, he will be accused of being over-cautious. If he refuses to give his approval, it will not be difficult for the management to find another technical expert who will approve. Yet if he remains silent, someone else will get the blame if anything goes wrong. So he says nothing.

It is therefore essential in any organisation dealing with potentially dangerous events to have an independent body with the power to stop immediately any process that they consider unsafe, without any argument. This already exists for nuclear reactors.

Anyone with responsibilities for a large organisation, not excluding the Church, needs to think very carefully to ensure that the structure of the organisation is such that the psychological pressures are in the direction of safety.

97. WILL THE WORLD POPULATION GO UP OR DOWN?

It has been remarked that it is always difficult to be a prophet, especially about the future. Nevertheless we all want to know, at least in broad outlines, what the future holds. Indeed we must know, if we are to make prudent plans to avoid looming dangers and ensure that civilisation continues. Scientists have not been slow in predicting future trends, but it must seem to the general reader that they cannot make up their minds. This greatly reduces the credibility of science, and also makes any sensible planning impossible.

Just to take two examples, a few years ago we were told that the earth is cooling, and we will eventually all freeze to death. Now we are told that the earth is warming up, and that the consequences will be catastrophic. Then again we have demographers telling us that the population of the world is rapidly increasing, so that human needs will soon outrun the resources of the earth. No sooner have we begun to think what we can do about this, when we are told by another group of experts that world population is imploding due to the falling birth rate.

What are we to think about such contradictory forecasts, and many others? Let us just consider the population problem. It is undeniable that over the last century the population of the world has increased rapidly; it is doubling about every thirty-five years. If this goes on we will clearly be in serious trouble at some time during the present century. However on a closer look we find that the rates of increase of population in various countries are very different. In Africa and South America it is much higher than in Europe and North America, so each country must be considered separately.

If we know the present population of a country and the birth and death rate, we can easily predict the future population, assuming that the rates remain the same. Thus we can show that in a century or two Italy will be populated mainly by Tunisians and Moroccans. The flaw in this argument is that it assumes that the birth and death rates will remain unchanged, whereas it is very likely that they will change for a variety of reasons, and this will strongly affect the forecasts. Most of these reasons are unknown, and this accounts for the large differences between forecasts.

It is however well known that the birthrate in poor countries is high, and gradually decreases as the standard of living increases. This has already happened in Europe. If it happens worldwide, and if the standard of living increases, then it is likely that the world population will eventually stabilise. Already the rate of increase of world population is slowing down. At present the world population is about six billion, and computer calculations indicate that it may stabilise at about twice this number in the middle of the century.

It is interesting to compare this with the estimate of the maximum number of people that the earth can support. This depends on many factors that are difficult to determine, so the estimates range from 6 to 150 billion, with the favoured value around 8 to 12 billion. This is very similar to the estimates of the actual population around 2050. If the world population exceeds the carrying capacity of the earth, the result will be such serious damage to the environment that the earth will be able to support only a small fraction of its present population.

These estimates provide much food for thought.

98.   SCIENCE IN THE SERVICE OF MANKIND

The primary aim of scientists is to find out more about the world and to understand how it works. To do this they observe the world as carefully as possible, and make measurements wherever practicable. The next stage is to test ideas about the processes that might be going on behind the appearances, and then to test them by comparing their consequences with what has been observed and measured. If there are any differences, the scientist has to alter the ideas in a systematic way and test them again. In this way we gradually come to understand the world in ever more detail.

It is very often found that this new knowledge about the world has useful applications. It may help us to grow more food, cure our illnesses or make new machines. This makes it clear to everyone that science is useful as well as interesting, and then people are more ready to support the work of the scientist. This is vital for the continuation of science, especially as the necessary equipment for scientific research becomes more and more expensive.

There is now, however, an increasing tendency to judge scientific research, and hence the level of funding, by its likely practical applications. When scientists submit a research proposal they are often required to specify the benefits that will come if the research is successful. This seems very reasonable: if society pays, then surely society has a right to expect some return. Scientists cannot expect to be given large amounts of money just to satisfy their idle curiosity.

This view of the relation between science and human society has a long history. It was vigorously propagated about sixty years ago by the Marxist physicist J.D. Bernal. He said that the state must set the priorities for scientific research, and the whole scientific enterprise must be organised to maximise the benefit to society. The most important social problems must be identified, and teams of scientists given the task of solving them.

These ideas were strongly opposed by Michael Polanyi, G.P. Thomson and many other scientists. They emphasised that the primary purpose of science is the discovery of truth, and research must be directed towards this end. The central importance of truth has recently been re-emphasised by the Pope in his encyclical *Fides et Ratio*.

If this is forgotten, not only will science itself wither, but so will the flow of useful applications. The reason for this is simply that it is not possible to foresee the applications of any piece of scientific research. An investigation, carried out in order to understand some aspect of nature, may lead to applications that are totally unexpected. Examples are legion. Rutherford, pioneer of nuclear physics, said in 1936 that he could foresee no more than small-scale applications of atomic energy. If Roentgen had set out to improve the treatment of wounds, he would never have discovered X-rays. If Madame Curie had not aimed to find a way to cure cancer, she would never have discovered radium. Michael Faraday found out how to make an electric current turn a wheel, and was asked whether it was any use. It was the first electric motor.

The importance of supporting disinterested research does not mean that scientists must always be given whatever support they want. Research proposals need to be examined by independent experts, and the ability of the proposers assessed. This is quite different from the demand that the proposal be socially relevant in some way. This is simply absurd, and is the sure road to mediocrity.

99.   FACTS AND VALUES

Values are essential if we are to know where we want to go, but if we do not also have a firm grasp of the facts we may never get there.

I was once asked to justify my statement that statistical studies show that the (so-called) benign renewable energy sources are comparatively dangerous. It is of course very important to ensure that our energy supplies are obtained as safely as possible. To obtain information on this, studies have been made of the numbers of deaths and injuries associated with the generation of a thousand megawatt years of electricity using various energy sources. Included in this were the deaths due to the processes used to obtain the raw materials, those due to the construction and maintenance of the power stations and to the distribution of electricity to the consumers. The dangers included mining accidents, oil well and oil rig fires, the collapse of dams and radioactive hazards.

The results for the numbers of deaths were: coal 40, oil 10, wind 5, solar 5, hydroelectric 3, nuclear 1 and natural gas 0.3. Inevitably, for a number of reasons, these figures are subject to an uncertainty of about a factor of two, but they agree with other similar studies and the ranking order is very probably correct.

The benign renewables are relatively hazardous because a large number of windmills or solar panels have to be made to give the same energy output as a coal, oil or nuclear power station. The materials used in their construction have to be made in factories and the construction and maintenance hazards are considerable.

Safety is not the only aspect to be considered in the assessment of a power source. We should also assess its reliability, cost and effect on the environment. The renewables are unreliable because the wind does not always blow and the sun does not always shine, so it is necessary to provide a back-up generator in case of need. If, however, the backup is better in many respects than the renewables, then we may well ask why we have the renewables at all. Despite many improvements, the renewable sources are still relatively costly and since they tap thinly spread energy they inevitably require large areas of prominent land. Opinions vary about the aesthetic qualities of the renewables, but most people still dislike large numbers of huge windmills or arrays of solar panels. Particularly affected are those who have moved far into the countryside for peace and quiet and are driven to distraction by the constant humming sound from arrays of windmills. They cannot escape because their home has become unsaleable. It is better for the countryside to have a small number of carefully-sited coal or oil or nuclear power stations.

Another environmental effect is pollution. Coal, gas and oil power stations pollute the atmosphere with carbon dioxide (alleged to cause global warming) and a range of other chemicals that fall as acid rain and ruin forests, lakes and rivers. It is strange that it is never admitted by the environmentalists that nuclear power stations are the most benign.

It is also an important consideration to conserve chemicals that are needed by our industries. It is most wasteful to burn valuable oil, and also to consume gas and oil that may also be needed. By contrast, uranium and thorium, burnt in nuclear reactors, have no other large-scale uses.

For these and many other reasons, the submission of the Holy See to the International Conference on Nuclear Power held in Vienna in 1982 stressed that "all possible efforts should be made to extend to all countries, especially the developing ones, the benefits contained in the peaceful uses of nuclear energy."

A detailed discussion, with extensive statistics, may be found in my book *Nuclear Power, Energy and the Environment*, recently published by the Imperial College Press.

100. IT'S ALL IN THE NUMBERS

The great nineteenth century physicist Lord Kelvin once remarked that "if you cannot measure what you are talking about and express it in numbers, your knowledge is of a most meagre and unsatisfactory kind." Of course this only applies to what can be measured, and this includes subjects that are vital for our well-being and for the future of our society. Among these are highly controversial matters like mad cow disease, the health risks of mobile phones, nuclear radiations and the best way to ensure our continuing energy supplies. All too often these and similar subjects are treated in the media on purely emotional lines. Particular incidents are described in harrowing detail and then very general conclusions are drawn. Those who disagree are likely to make a similar emotional response, and the debate is just one assertion against another, with no possibility of reaching agreement about the truth.

In such cases the only way to reach the truth is to express the measurable aspects in numbers. For example in the case of mobile phones, it is necessary to measure the electromagnetic fields they generate and compare them with the fields that we experience all the time, such as those from other electrical appliances, and from the sun. If the fields due to the phones are relatively small, then they are unlikely to be harmful.

To take another example, some people say that wind power is the answer to our energy needs, while others say that the power that can be produced in this way is so small that windmills are unable to solve our energy problems. This argument can only be settled by measuring the power output of typical wind turbines and comparing it with our known energy needs. We then find that it needs about a thousand very large wind turbines to equal the power output of a coal power station. In addition, their output fluctuates with the wind speed and so is very unreliable. It is also expensive, dangerous and harmful to the environment. It is then no surprise that wind contributes only about a fifth of a per cent of our energy in Britain.

When we talk about the dangers of various power sources, these can also be expressed numerically. No energy source is perfectly safe; all are dangerous in one way or another, and so it is possible to gather statistics of the number of workers killed and injured to produce a certain amount of electricity. We then find that coal is by far the most dangerous, followed by oil, then wind, solar and hydro, with gas and nuclear the safest. Without the numbers, no useful conclusions can ever be reached.

It is always very easy to make an impressive case against this or that source of energy, or new process, by emphasising the dangers and other disadvantages, but to reach a balanced conclusion it is necessary to express them in numbers, and compare these numbers with the corresponding numbers for other sources.

Similarly for other hazards like mad cow disease. We must certainly do all we can to reduce the dangers to a minimum, but then we have to compare them with other similar dangers. We are then likely to find that quite familiar activities like driving a car or crossing the road, are indeed far more dangerous. Unless we make a numerical estimate of the dangers, we are likely to spend our time avoiding minuscule dangers while exposing ourselves to much more serious dangers.

So the next time you see a scare story, look for the numbers. If there are none, it is very likely that there is no solid evidence to support the allegations, and they can be ignored as worse than useless. This applies particularly to people who write indignant letters to newspapers. It is unfortunately the case that the less they know, the more emphatic they become and, regrettably, ignorance and discourtesy often go together.

GENERAL REFERENCES

The Encyclopedia of Philosophy, Macmillan and Free Press, 1967.

W.E. Bynum, E.J. Browne and Roy Porter (Ed.), *Dictionary of the History of Science, Macmillan,* 1981.

P.E. Hodgson, *Nuclear Power, Energy and the Environment,* London: Imperial College Press, 1999.

S.L. Jaki, *The Relevance of Physics,* Chicago University Press, 1966.

S.L. Jaki, *Science and Creation,* Scottish Academic Press, 1974.

S.L. Jaki, *The Road of Science and the Ways to God,* Chicago University Press, 1978.

Karl A. Kneller, *Christianity and the Leaders of Modern Science,* Real View Books, 1995.

Colin A. Ronan, *The Cambridge Illustrated History of the World's Science,* Cambridge University Press, 1983.

REFERENCES AND NOTES

1. Discourse to the Pontifical Academy of Sciences, 10th November 1979.
2. Address to UNESCO and the United Nations, 1990.
3. Address to a General Audience in 1986.
4. Address to a Study Week in 1982.
   Homily on the Feast of St John Gualbert, 1990.
5. Address to the Regional Council of Lazio, 1991.
6. Conference on Faith and Science, Rome, 22nd–23rd May, 2000.
7. Dorothy L. Sayers, *The Mind of the Maker*, London: Methuen, 1941.
8. Stanley L. Jaki, *The Bible and Science*, Christendom Press, 1996.
9, 10. Stanley L. Jaki, *Genesis I through the Ages*, Thomas More Press, 1992.
11. Stanley L. Jaki, *The Saviour of Science*, Gateway, 1988.
12. Alexis Carrel, *The Voyage to Lourdes, With an Introduction by Stanley L. Jaki*, Real View Books, 1994.
13. Stanley L. Jaki, *God and the Sun at Fatima*, Real View Books, 1999.
14. Stanley L. Jaki, *Miracles and Physics*, Christendom Press, 1989.
15. Fritjof Capra, *The Tao of Physics*, Wildwood House, 1975.
    R.B. Crease and C.C. Mann in *Philosophy of Science and the Occult* (Ed. P. Grin), State University of New York Press, 1990.
17. Stanley L. Jaki, *Science and Creation*, Edinburgh: Scottish Academic Press, 1974.
18. P.E. Hodgson, *The Christian Origin of Science*, First Coyne Lecture, 1997.
    Logos, 4:2, Spring 2001.
20. Stanley L. Jaki, *The Relevance of Physics*, Chicago University Press, 1966.
21. Toby E. Huff, *The Rise of Early Modern Science: Islam, China and the West*, Cambridge University Press, 1993.
23. R. Sorabji (Ed.), *Philoponus and the Rejection of Aristotelian Science*, Duckworth, 1987.
24. James A. Weisheipl (Ed.), *Albertus Magnus and the Sciences, Commemorative Essays 1980*, Pontifical Institute of Medieval Studies, Toronto.

25. A.C. Crombie, *Robert Grosseteste and the Origins of Experimental Science,* Oxford University Press, 1953.
James McEvoy, *The Philosophy of Robert Grosseteste,* Oxford University Press, 1982.

26. R.W. Southern, *Robert Grosseteste,* Oxford University Press, 1986.

27. Angus Armitage, *The World of Copernicus,* EP Publishing, 1951.

28. Giordano Bruno, *The Ash Wednesday Supper: La Cena de le Ceneri, Translated with an Introduction and Notes by Stanley L. Jaki,* Mouton, 1975.
Frances A. Yates, *Giordano Bruno and the Hermetic Tradition,* Routledge and Kegan Paul, 1964.

29–31. Vincent F. Blehl (Ed.), *The Essential Newman,* Mentor-Omega Books, 1963.
Ernan McMullin, *Galileo: Man of Science,* Basic Books, 1967.
Michael Sharratt, *Galileo: Decisive Innovator,* Blackwell, 1994.

32. Richard S. Westfall, *Never at Rest: A Biography of Isaac Newton,* Cambridge University Press, 1980.

33. E.K. Palsson, *Niels Stensen: Scientist and Saint,* tr. M.N.L. Couve de Murville, Oscott Series No. 2, Dublin: Veritas, 1988.
J.E. Poulson and E. Snorrason (Ed.), *Nickolaus Steno 1638–1686: A Re-Consideration by Danish Scientists,* Genofte, 1986.

35. Karl A. Kneller, *Christianity and the Leaders of Modern Science,* Real View Books, 1995.

36. Frederick Kurzer, *Annals of Science,* 56.1113.1999.

37. F. McGrath, *Newman's University: Ideal and Reality,* Longmans Green, 1971.
J.H. Newman, *The Idea of a University,* Longmans Green, 1947.
J.H. Newman, *An Essay in Aid of a Grammar of Assent,* Longmans Green 1947.
J.H. Newman, *Letters and Diaries,* Oxford University Press.

38. J.R. Lucas, *Wilberforce and Huxley: A Legendary Encounter, The Historical Journal,* 22.313.1979.

39. Stanley L. Jaki, *Uneasy Genius: The Life and Work of Pierre Duhem,* Martinus Nijhoff,1984.
Stanley L. Jaki, *Scientist and Catholic: Pierre Duhem,* Christendom Press, 1991.
Stanley L. Jaki, *Reluctant Heroine: The Life and Work of Hélène Duhem,* Scottish Academic Press, 1992.

40.   A. Pais, *Subtle is the Lord: The Science and the Life of Albert Einstein,* Oxford University Press, 1982.

41.   "L'Academie Pontificale des Sciences en Mémoire de son Second Président Georges Lemaître à L'Occasion du Cinquième Anniversaire de sa Mort", *Pontificiae Academiae Scientiarum Scripta Varia,* No. 36, 1972.
       G.C. McVittie, Obituary, Quarterly Journal of the Royal Astronomical Society, 8.294.1967.
       Jozef Turek, "Georges Lemaître and the Pontifical Academy of Sciences", *Specola Vaticana,* Vol. 2, No. 13, 1989.

42.   Douglas McKie, *Nature,* 28th April, 1956, p. 794
       E.J. Holmyard, *Ambix,* Vol. 5. Nos. 3 and 4, October 1956, p. 57.

43.   A.C. Crombie, *Augustine to Galileo: The History of Science A.D. 400–1650,* Falcon, 1952.
       A.C. Crombie (Ed.), *Scientific Change,* Heinemann, 1963.
       A.C. Crombie, *Science, Optics and Music in Medieval and Early Modern Thought,* Hambledon Press, 1990.
       A.C. Crombie, *Styles of Scientific Thinking in the European Tradition,* Duckworth, 1994.
       A.C. Crombie, *Science, Art and Nature in Medieval and Modern Thought,* Hambledon Press, 1996.

44.   M. Goldsmith, *Sage: A Life of J.D. Bernal,* Hutchinson, 1980.

46.   J. Crewdson, *Christian Doctrine in the Light of Michael Polanyi's Theology of Personal Knowledge,* E. Mellon, 1994.

47–60. P.E. Hodgson, *Nuclear Power, Energy and the Environment,* Imperial College Press, 1999.
       P.E. Hodgson, "Global Warming and Nuclear Power", *Nuclear Energy,* 38.147.1999.

49.   J.H. Fremlin, *Power Production: What are the Risks?,* Oxford University Press, 1987.

55.   Sir Ghillian Prance, *The Earth under Threat,* Wild Goose Publications, Saint Andrew Press, 1996.

61.   J.R. Lucas and P.E. Hodgson, *Spacetime and Electromagnetism,* Oxford, 1990.

62, 63. L.E.Ballentine, "The Statistical Interpretation of Quantum Mechanics", *Reviews of Modern Physics,* 42.358.1970.

T.A. Brody, *The Philosophy behind Physics,* Luis de la Pena and P.E. Hodgson (Ed.), Springer-Verlag, 1993.

K.R. Popper, *Quantum Theory and the Schism in Physics,* W.W. Barclay (Ed.), Hutchinson, 1956.

64. Stanley L. Jaki, *Is there a Universe?,* Liverpool University Press, 1993.

65. P.E. Hodgson, *Cosmology and Theology,* The Second Coyne Lecture, 1995.

66. Stanley L. Jaki, *Cosmos and Creator,* Edinburgh: Scottish Academic Press, 1980.

67. William Lane Craig and Quentin Smith, *Theism, Atheism and Big Bang Cosmology,* Oxford University Press, 1993.

68. Stanley L. Jaki, *God and the Cosmologists,* Edinburgh: Scottish Academic Press, 1989, Second Edition, Real View Books, 1998.

69. J.D. Barrow and F.J. Tipler, *The Anthropic Cosmological Principle,* Oxford: Clarendon Press, 1986.

70. E. Broda, *Ludwig Boltzmann,* Oxbow Press, 1983.
Carlo Cercignani, *Ludwig Boltzmann,* Oxford University Press, 1998.

71. A.C. Crombie, *Styles of Scientific Thinking in the European Tradition: The History of Argument and Explanation especially in the Mathematical and Biomedical Sciences and Arts,* London: Duckworth, 1996.

74. Philip Kitcher, *Abusing Science: The Case Against Creationism,* Open University Press, 1983.

75. Thomas Kuhn, *The Structure of Scientific Revolutions,* Chicago University Press, 1963, Second Edition, 1970.

77. Allan Bloom, *The Closing of the American Mind,* Penguin, 1997.
Michael Dummett, "The Intellectual Standing of Philosophy", *Oxford Magazine,* Noughth Week, Michaelmas Term 1998.

78. Jean Bricmont, "Science Studies – What's Wrong?", *Physics World,* December 1997, p. 15.
Alan Sokal and Jean Bricmont, *Intellectual Impostors,* Profile Books, 1998.
Alan Sokal and Jean Bricmont, "The Naked Postmodernists", *Times Higher,* 10th October, 1997, p. 22.

87,89. "The Place of the Scientist in the Life of the Church", Papers presented at the meeting of the Secretariat for Scientific Questions, *Pax Romana,* St Albans, 1998.

98.   P.E. Hodgson, "Science in the Service of Mankind", *South African Journal of Physics,* 2nd January 1997.

M. Polanyi, *The Contempt of Freedom,* Watts, 1940.

M. Polanyi, *Personal Knowledge,* Routledge and Kegan Paul, 1958.

96.   Richard Feynman, *What Do You Care What Other People Think?,* W.W. Norton and Co., 2001.

ACKNOWLEDGEMENTS

In addition to the Editor of the *Catholic Herald,* I thank the Editors of the following journals for permission to reprint articles and book reviews: *Catholic Dossier* (85, 92), *Contemporary Review* (50), *International Philosophical Quarterly* (67), *Modern Age* (8), *The Month* (54, 55, 62), *New Blackfriars* (71) , *Science and Religion Forum Reviews* (46,64), *The Tablet* (17, 20, 66, 68), *Theology* (74).

NAME INDEX

Witelow, 150.
Wright, Thomas, 133.

Yates, Francis, 65, 207.

Zuckerman, Solly (Lord), 91.
Zycinski, Archbishop Josef, 5, 180.

SUBJECT INDEX

Subjectivism, 128, 142, 163–164.
Sufficient reason, principle of, 61, 140.
Sugar, 78.
Sunspots, 68, 151.
Symmetries of nature, 19, 168.

Taoism, 40.
Technology, control of, 185.
Ten Commandments, 166.
Telescope, 49, 66–67, 135, 150.
Theology and science, 5, 28, 40, 47, 52, 55, 60, 70, 80, 83, 86, 89, 127, 141, 143, 154–155.
Thermodynamics, second law, 145–146.
Tides, argument from, 64, 66, 70.
Time, 71–72, 128, 139, 145–146.
Tokai-Mura accident, 121–123.
Torus fusion devices, 97.
Trinity, 21–23, 79, 89, 91, 171.
Truth, importance of, 188, 200.

Uniformity of nature, 34, 39, 166–167.
United Nations, 13, 115, 206.
Universe, 133–146, 159.
University education, 79.

Values, 201.
Vienna Circle, 93, 129.

Wave power, 120, 170.
Wave theory of light, 157.
Weather prediction, 174.
Wind power, 104, 109, 112, 117, 120, 170, 201, 203.
Windscale reactor accident, 196.
World as organism, 26–27, 50.
World Health Organisation, 101.

X-rays, 186, 191, 200.
X-ray picture, 90, 162.

Zeeman effect, 92.